Myth and Mischief
in Allenby Park

ISBN 978-0-9570892-2-8 (paperback edition)

British Library Cataloguing in Publication Data
A catalogue for this title is available at the British Library

Characters and events in this book have been inspired by a house that once stood on the site of Allenby Park, in Felixstowe, and one of its occupants, Field Marshall Viscount 1st of Megiddo and Felixstowe, Lord Allenby (1880-1936).
The stories are works of fiction.

Commissioning Editor Dominique Roche

Allenby Park watercolour by Charles Nightingale
Allenby Park gate and mansion images by Charles Nightingale
Portrait of Joan by Charles Nightingale
www.charleynightingale.com

Design, layout, and children's cartoon images by Diane Rich

Printed and bound in the United Kingdom by
Tuddenham Press Ltd
Unit 4, Hill Farm Barns, Ashbocking Road, Henley, Suffolk IP6 0SA

First printing July 2020

Published by 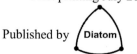 Diatom

Copies are available from diatom@hotmail.co.uk
and **Stillwater Books**
www.stillwaterfelixstowe.co.uk • 01394 548010

For Joan

Myth and Mischief in Allenby Park

by Lesley Glaister, Robin Greene,

Charles Nightingale, Luke Nightingale,

and Diane Rich

with foreword by Dominique Roche

Contents

*Poems by **Luke Nightingale** are from:
The Price of Progress and Other Poems (2009)

Foreword

These stories started in the winter of 2018 when my friend Joan was given a watercolour entitled, *Allenby Park*. It was presented as a gift for her 100th birthday, and a group of us gathered in her lounge to toast the hanging of the artwork. As well as me, there were: Charles Nightingale - the artist who created the painting, Robin Greene - the first person to fall in love with it, and Diane Rich - a former neighbour who knew Allenby Park well.

Joan studied the painting. Her twins used to play in Allenby Park, and she had often taken my own children there. Even though they have all grown up, Joan still loves to walk in amongst the trees, the squirrels, and the budding footballers. With glee she said, 'That's it!' and grabbed some invisible thing in the air, laughing, 'You're it!' as if she was about to sprint off with the children in the painting. She is the most mischievous child I know. We followed her lead.

Diane laughed, remembering the games she shared there with her twin brother and their school mates. Charles had nostalgic visions of his two sons running past the gates to meet their friends. One of them, Luke, features in the painting as an eight-year-old boy, later to become a poet. Robin spoke of parks loved with a passion throughout family life, from Surrey to Yorkshire and Felixstowe.

As the nights grew longer, stories about the house began to take a twist. Diane recalled someone once trying to deliver a letter to 41, Constable Road. After directing them to the odd numbers in the street, where the house should be, she went looking for it herself but only found numbers 39 and 43. There was no number 41. In its place were park gates, leading to Allenby Park. Was there ever a house numbered 41? Why wasn't it there? Who were the Allenbys?

Coincidences and mysteries began to grow like wild plants we hadn't seen before. It was as if we had walked into Charles' picture and creatures of the imagination – ghosts, beasts, genies, baddies – had been lurking there waiting for us. We were running in the park again, free to play; we were telling each other tales. I didn't want the fun to end, so I suggested that we make a book of our stories. By then, the well-known author Lesley Glaister, who once lived in a house backing onto the park, had joined in the game too.

This book is made of three poems and four stories as different as the minds of each person who ever walks through the unnumbered gates. They are just stories - an escape through the mythical horn and ivory gates of dreams - but if you like them, Allenby Park will never be the same again.

by *Dominique Roche*

The Dreamers

We fly so close to the sun

In an open sky ready for more,

And then I have these wings

I built them for two,

But I can't even lift myself.

by *Luke Nightingale*

Through the Fence

When I was ten, my family moved to Felixstowe, to a house that backed onto a park. A park with a gateway and big iron gates but we didn't need the gateway. All we had to do was sidle through a gap in the fence and we were in.

I thought of Narnia as I first squeezed through shrubs, emerged from the gap and stood between the trunks of massive copper beeches. Later, lying on our lawn, revising for 'O' and 'A' levels I'd roll onto my back to gaze at the summer leaves printed red against the blue, the wrong colour for leaves, like Christmas sherry.

Our garden was a rectangle of lawn and flowerbeds, regular and tidy, the park a spilling out, a freedom, a field of possibilities. Although it was a municipal park, it also felt like mine; more mine than most people's because I could just step through. I was possessive. It was more our park than anyone else's. Possessive but generous; they could use it too.

We had a brain-damaged dog once, Daisy, who would get out through the fence and then be lost; so many times she was returned home, looking loopy with her lip caught up on her teeth or one of her ears inside out. Dad said he'd nail the gap up, but he never did.

In that park I made mud-faced snowmen; I hid and cried; I hid and spied; I crunched through leaves and took them home to press between the pages of Dickens. I used to swing so high the frame would jolt, hang my head back to see the world upside down, hair trailing in the dust. When I was older it was the evenings that were best; the shady time, when the mothers and babies had gone and under the trees and within the bushes, beginners roamed and clustered: beginner smokers, beginner lovers. I remember the iron tang of swing chain on my hands along with tobacco smoke and the rocking of the witch's hat – a tall pointed roundabout – making me feel glamorously sick. Boys would run it round till it span and lurched and my friends and I, unimpressed, would cling. I remember a bench of graffiti carved deep in green gloss paint, sitting there cold and nervous while a boy inched his hand along the back. I remember a first startlingly sloppy kiss. I remember squeezing through at night when I was meant to be in my room, thinking myself alone, lighting up a miserable Players No6, then hearing rustling, a man's cough, and in panic shooting back through the fence, grinding the cigarette into the soil, and panting, as if I'd just escaped something big. Going back into the lit sitting room, the family watching TV seemed insulated from the possibilities out there; they hadn't even noticed I'd been gone.

I had a bedroom downstairs with French windows that opened onto the garden: the garden opened onto the park, so that I could never feel quite easy in my bed. If I could step in and out of the park at will, so could anyone. There was only glass between that anyone and me. It was frightening and a thrill. A hamster lived at large in that room, making nests from the velvet curtains, waking me in the night by scampering across my bed. Once, with friends, I held a séance there and whatever we summoned never left. Once, when my parents were out an illicit boy came round, and when the front door opened, he crept out of the French windows and melted off into the park, into the dark.

Now my garden in Edinburgh has solid walls around it; a hedgehog could not get through, much less a child. But if Allenby Park was there, if I could sidle in each day and sample the seasons, sway on a swing, drift among the trees, I wonder if I'd meet my awkward, fearful, fascinated child-self there, hair in the dust, world flashing upside down as she swung till the whole frame jolted.

by *Lesley Glaister*

Lost in the Park

I hadn't been in Allenby Park for about twenty years. For one thing, it's haunted. For another, any adult male who ventures by himself into a small park with swings and other children's amusements, wants his brains examined. But it had been calling to me more and more urgently. I took to reading about it, and its history.

I had learned that an imposing mansion once stood where the entrance to the Park is. It was pulled down by its owner, when his mother died, and the associated land became a public park named after him. I was aged eight when I first heard of General Allenby in connection with the crusades. At the time these events were presented as a valiant, but unsuccessful attempt by the Christian nations of Europe to recapture the Holy Places of Palestine from the Arab conquerors of Jerusalem during the twelfth century. Caliph Omar had received the surrender of the city from the Byzantine Christian Patriarch Sophronius in 637 AD. Omar is said to have declined to pray with Sophronius in the Church of the Holy Sepulchre, on the grounds that he wanted it to remain a place of Christian worship and thought that his entering of the church would signal to his people that it had become a mosque. I like to believe this story. When reading history, I choose to believe such plausible lies or implausible truth as feature the greatest acts of nobility, to try to be more optimistic about human nature than I am in my everyday affairs. The current narrative is that the crusades were a cover for a barbaric attack on a peaceful people, by rapacious thugs, indulging in murderous bloodshed and pillage under the guise of fearless faith, for power and gain.

The story of the third crusade at the end of the twelfth century was our main sustenance, with the sieges of Acre, Tyre and finally Jerusalem, featuring a sort of middle-ages superhero in Richard the Lionheart, and an arch-villain in the form of Saladin who got the last laugh: the siege of Jerusalem failed. Saladin also figured in an anecdote where Richard was showing off by severing a rock in half, with one sweep of his mighty sword. In riposte, Saladin invited Richard to do the same with a silk cushion; however hard he tried, he couldn't. Saladin then quickly dispatched it with his scimitar. So, the third crusade, like most of them, was a flop. But we were told, in a way which had the feel of a patriotic, off-curriculum face saver, that success *was* achieved about eight hundred years later when guess who, 'swept down' on Jerusalem, in a sub plot of the Great Massacre of 1914-1918? None other than the owner of the park mansion, which had been known as Felixstowe House: Viscount of Megiddo and Felixstowe – Lord Allenby!

The park thus became Allenby Park, in honour of this soldier who, once in Jerusalem, like his Islamic forbear, took pains to prevent local Christians attacking the mosques of his defeated enemies. He used the simple but effective plan of sending some cohorts of Muslim troops from parts of his diverse imperial army to act as guards for these places of worship. In accordance with my code, plausible lie or implausible truth, I believe in his attempt to respect the beliefs of the losing side in what was in part anyway, a religious war.

I was tense and watchful as I crossed the road and walked uneasily toward the park entrance. There was a strange singing in my ears – something that usually strikes only at random. It seemed to grow as the distance between me and the gates shrank. I suffer from an illness called *Nostalgitis*. I have it in a fairly acute form, and my walk toward the park was analogous to an alcoholic's walk to the pub, when their partner is elsewhere - foolhardy and dangerous. But then the same could be said of Allenby's sweep down on Jerusalem; not that I could be said to be sweeping down on the park... gliding was more like it.

Many years had passed since I last went through the park gates with my own young boys. The nostalgitis was growing and made my ears ring. Remember Scotty and his warp drive? He could whisk his spaceship across the light years in minutes, thus violating Einstein's principle that nothing can exceed the speed of light. I have my own drive called the Nostalgia drive, and I guess it has got strong enough to jump the warp to nearby space-time, like a wandering bum jumping the freight to cover the miles across the American plains. I was about to do the same when the ringing in my ears intensified. The crew of the Starship Enterprise didn't all get ringing in the ears when Scotty used the dilithium crystals to enter warp drive, did they? The happy band seemed to sail across the dark light years in perfect comfort. I reckon I was going faster than the Enterprise. There was a sudden change as I moved through the iron gates, which were wide open.

A strangely familiar but overwhelming smell invaded my brain and I momentarily swayed, as if I was inebriated. Its power was such that my other senses seemed to blend with this intense olfactory miasma and rose to the level of a new sense altogether. Perhaps it is the sense which comes to artists, poets and musicians, but which had previously never come to me who has, it seems, no heart, only a tin substitute, and a steel soul.

I knew the smell very well. It was the intoxicating smell of Was from whence I come. Like the very first sniff I got of the first RAF camp I set foot in, which pervaded the whole RAF, the smell of Was was the base ingredient of all the smells of that lost and mourned world. Yet I wasn't in Was.

I saw the paths of the park that went nowhere, because they were already there. I saw ghosts; ghosts of the living, ghosts of the dead, ghosts of those who had never lived, ghosts of those who might have lived. I saw a mad-eyed ghost wearing a legal-looking wig who didn't know he was a ghost. I knew him better than most of the other ghosts. I saw a sad ghost in a muddy, khaki uniform, with regulation puttees, fear in the hollows of its grey threatening eyes. I saw one in a blue-grey uniform, which briefly glanced in my direction as if it could see me, a posed look of fragile false confidence in its uneasy face; I knew that ghost best of all. And I saw a ghost general, in desert uniform, riding breeches and leather boots, complete with pith helmet and Sam Browne. His eyes were gazing toward something I couldn't see; shadowy figures surrounding him gazed at him, as if he was the Messiah himself. He was indeed a striking figure. The archetype of an early twentieth century British Officer. Standing as straight as a ramrod, moustachioed face set in an expression of alert confident certainty, a man who would have quickly dispatched me with his revolver, should I display one flicker of insolence or insubordination.

My attention was caught suddenly by the mad-eyed ghost. He seemed to be moving toward me in a circuitous, almost sly manner. His expression was that of someone who has some news for you which he is right to suppose you need urgently to know. It is very bad news. But his face shows eager relish, under a phony look of sorrow and concern. I quickly mingled with some monks whom I recognised, out of his line of vision. They knew me and looked at me with friendly contempt. Only one smiled, and said, 'Jolly good'. Another glanced at me furtively, with something like a sneer in his eyes. I remembered his outrageously unjust remark, and still shrivelled up inside. It was Brother Rogation. Now he was repeating another hurtful comment he had once made. He had just praised Dillon for getting 90% on a test. I had said, 'He *would*' in a sneering voice. Rogation snapped out his response. 'Yes – *he* would: some *do*, and some *don't*, and you won't.'

He had been right then. Dillon went to Oxford. He had been wrong the other time though. He had called me a bit of a bully when I had been forced against my will to enter a boxing tournament and, in a blind panic, given another boy a severe beating.

'To damnation with Rogation,' I thought.

I slunk away, at least having seemingly given the mad-eyed ghost the slip. I scanned the distant horizon and thought I saw Them, still more light years away, which seemed illogical. The further away they were, the nearer they seemed. Nearby, there was someone I recognised. She smiled hopefully, as she always had. I smiled back into the face of someone who had loved me with a love that was never returned. She had called me a crazy fool, and a barmy idiot. 'Mummy is not going to make you any more ice creams,' she had said, tears streaming from her eyes. 'And you haven't got a conservatory either'. Now she was pointing at Them. 'I'll come with you if you like.' Just as she had come to watch football with me; and cricket; Surrey v the Australians. But already she was fading, like any well-behaved ghost.

I suddenly realised that I could never reach Them. I could just make them out, a group of boys on the limit of visibility. This place wasn't Was. 'You can't get to Was any more than you can get to Oz,' I thought. 'But it isn't Is either. What it actually is, is Isn't.' And I knew with instinctive certainty, where I would end up if I stayed here: in Wasn't; and I knew what Wasn't was. It has another, more commonplace name. And you can't get back from Wasn't.

I looked around desperately for some way out, or someone who knew the way out. And I saw a policeman. And beside him was Frankie, with whom I had fallen in futile love, as she had sat on a hydrogen bomb, conducting a fitness training session with a flight of WAAFs. They were looking in my direction.

I walked self-consciously toward them. I felt a mixture of guilt and gratitude. The feeling came from the policeman, nothing at all came from Frankie; it never had, but she looked at me kindly enough, and I saw that she had wings folded behind her back. I knew, when I saw them, that she was actually a ghost of a ghost. I wanted to address the policeman. 'It wasn't me. They did it for me without my knowledge or consent.' But before I could, all speech was drowned out by a Vulcan taxiing past, sending a chill down my spine. I ran frantically toward it, making throat cutting gestures, and sure enough it began to slow down. If it took off, I might be committing manslaughter – its Alt5 low-level altimeter would tell them it was at two hundred feet, even if they were only two inches from touching the ground. I felt a huge relief after the fifty or so years had passed since I had last seen it. But I never saw it stop; another impending doom arrived at the same time. I turned to the policeman. I was in Penge. I was filling my V8 with fuel, whose red colour branded it as RAF property. Airmen stealing fuel went to prison. He took time to appraise the situation very carefully, looking at my kit-bag in the back of the V8.

'In the RAF are you, sir? Bit of a show going on at the moment isn't there, sir?'

Like everyone else he knew we were in the middle of a Berlin crisis. He also knew what red petrol meant.

'Yes, I've been called back to camp.'

He looked again, ruminating over the scene, and then at me.

'Right, sir,' he said. 'Tanking up for the road?' He stared at the jerry can.

'Yes but… er,' I replied, in a desperate voice, petrified with fear that he would arrest me.

Then Frankie spoke. 'Don't make it so obvious,' she said, but pointed as she spoke. I remembered her saying that to Radcliffe as he climbed out of the window of the drying room to join her. She had knocked on it suggestively, whilst the Friday poker session was in full swing, and to my great pain they disappeared into the night, arm in arm.

The policeman pondered, then spoke, looking into my eyes. 'I would move on if I was you, sir,' he said in a stern calm voice. 'You need to get away from here.' I was sure he must once have been a real Squadron Man. I was on 83 Squadron, but was not really an accredited Squadron Man. I would have given up a month's salary to be one. But then I had missed that open goal, when we lost to OCU, which was Radcliffe's unit, in whose hangar Frankie usually exercised her WAAFs. And I bet Lt William Calley had been a Platoon Man and look where that led him - to My Lai. Camaraderie is the best thing, and the worst thing.

I looked in the direction Frankie indicated. Some distance away, a lone sunbeam was making landfall, illuminating a figure I knew very well. She was pushing a buggy, with its sunshade up. Hope shot through me and skirting the parked aircraft I ran toward her, but it was useless. By the time I was completely breathless, the figure was barely closer. I looked back; Frankie and the policeman were lost amongst other ghostly figures in the haze.

I began to panic, as if I had just run away from home to Tunbridge Wells. I had had too much of Isn't, but guessed I couldn't reach Was, whatever I did, and feared it would be easy to slip into Wasn't. Perhaps I was there already – perhaps this was what Wasn't was like. And I had walked into it from my obsession with Was. I resisted the temptation to weakly break down into tears, as I had done in Tunbridge Wells. But as I was standing shaking with fear, a loud stentorian voice sounded right in front of me.

'PULL YOURSELF TOGETHER MAN!'

I looked up into the face of Allenby. A stern, unyielding face, with not an iota of humanity in its expression... except... except something about the mouth... a rationality that reassured and invigorated. Automatically, I came to attention and up went my arm, longest way up shortest way down, as Corporal Shaw had explained to us. Allenby acknowledged the salute. 'Carry on Corporal,' he said quietly, and swept imperiously away.

'By the left, quick march!' barked Shaw. 'Left, left, left, right, left... y'had a good job butya left, elft, elft, elft...'

I hadn't had a good job, or any job, or any A levels either.

His voice faded as I marched away toward the figure with the pushchair, which I could see again. I didn't expect to reach her anymore but kept marching as strength returned to me. She was moving in such a manner that she always seemed to move at a slight angle to my trajectory, so that I had to frequently reorient my march toward her position. It was clear to me that Was was very gently rotating as she walked, but Isn't was not, and although she was walking more slowly than I, Was was picking up speed as it turned. It was as unreachable to me, as it would be. Yet I had confidence that I was marching in the right direction, and once the figure had dwindled to nothing, I marched on, straight-backed and in a straight line. I knew I couldn't get to Was, but I could find my way out of Isn't, if I kept my nerve. But my mind was still in Was.

The things I never said, I thought I'd say,
They linger in my heart like lines I fluffed,
I talked of this and that, and huffed and puffed,
I thought there'd always be a better day
I thought the way we were was here to stay,
And took too lightly all the chances muffed,
And failed to see the day the mainsail luffed,
Because the wind now blew the other way,
The path we trod from that old golden time,
Up which we shepherded our precious herd,
Yet never knowing where it really led,
Was long and hard and took me past my prime.
And my agenda - now so long deferred,
The things I thought I'd say! - I never said.

Of course, I never said it. I had said it before, to a gentle blameless creature and later stabbed her to the heart with the Dagger of Injustice, which gets a lot more employment than the Sword of Justice I should imagine.

I plodded on, doggedly and determinedly as straight as I could, in the uncertain and unstable world of Isn't. There's more to straight lines than you might think. Once, the Man with Fear in his Eyes – in happier times, before he was the Sad Ghost, and long after the fear had gone - had said to me, 'There's no such thing as a straight line!'

He had always come up with contradictory kinds of announcements like that; I mostly dismissed them as attention-seeking froth. But a friend of his had said to me, 'Nine things

26

out of ten that he says are piffle, but about one in ten can be very profound.' And later, I had found out that he was right about straight lines. It all depended on what was meant by straight. I knew enough to know that in the real world, the best you can do is a geodesic. And the pilot of a space rocket, who keeps the fiery exhaust behind so that it always looks like a bright blob and not like a curving line, is travelling along a geodesic. But it still comes back to where it started if the geodesic is a closed curve.

I kept looking back and made sure I kept my footprints aligned. Others of us – for there were many trying to escape from Isn't – walked very purposefully and directly but omitted this procedure and went off at slight angles, gradually veered off completely, and dropped back, fading as they went. I saw the anguish in their eyes as the haze engulfed them. I think they were getting the feeling of Wasn't.

Gradually I lost sight of all the others and seemed to be walking along the insubstantial streets of a small town. A tall house with a swimming pool inside brought on an attack of my *nostalgitis*, then came school buildings, ghosts of mothers with children, a room full of chess-players, sailing dinghies, boys and girls in blue, doing aerial kicks and strange dances, serious looking men sitting around polished tables with whiteboards covered in symbols, which I recalled from the mists of time, people in a pub with portfolios, a ceremony with a cat wrapped in cloth being interred; the town went on exposing its contents without restraint, rhyme or reason. Every nook and cranny

27

haunted by a ghost. But then the sound of Gabriel's horn - or was it a great ship's siren? - brought it to an end, and the town faded after its interminable ghostly review of Was. The Park reappeared, as a vast plane, which I recognised as Isn't.

I walked on through the increasingly dreary and wet fields of Isn't. But I could see that I was approaching its perimeter. Its walls were high and looked unscalable. Why had I entered this grim place? Why does the alcoholic go to the pub when his wife is out? Nostalgitics are just as weak. But my heart gave a little throb. I could see a gate ahead, along the wall. On an impulse, I looked back over my shoulder and saw that the mad-eyed ghost was following me like a bloodhound. It must have been tracking me ever since I left Brother Rogation.

It wore its wig, which seemed similar to a judicial wig, and it was close enough to speak in its thin reedy voice. 'It's no good you trying to escape from Isn't,' it said. 'You will never be free. What you deserve is Wasn't.'

'Shut up you damned sanctimonious ghost,' I shouted, before it got too close.

'I am *not* a ghost,' it screeched, reaching out with its *breaky* hand. '*You* are a ghost. And that's all you will ever be. You betrayed the crew of that Vulcan. You betrayed your loving...'

'I'm warning you ghost, shut up.'

It was close enough to almost touch me.

'You *are* a ghost,' it said. 'I can see right through you and so does everyone you know.'

I had the Scimitar of Saladin conveniently by my side. If it

28

could do silk cushions it could do ghosts.

'Take that! You *see-through* bastard,' I said as I tore through its substance with the scimitar. It dropped like a rotten pear, without a thud.

I broke into a run toward the blessed gates, tears coming from my eyes. My soul struggled to keep up with me. But as we arrived at the gigantic but beautiful wrought iron gates, I saw a figure who gestured to me to stop my desperate rush. He was dressed in something like a toga, in off-white, but wore an official looking peaked hat in the same colour.

'Stop!' he said.

'Can you open the gates?' I asked.

'I could,' he replied.

'Well will you?'

'I don't know.'

'Tell me what I need to do, to be allowed through.'

'Why should I let you?'

'I want to go back to Is, from whence I came; is Is through there?'

'You just told a lie. You can't go through.'

'What lie?'

'You said Is is through there. But it isn't Is.'

'No. I asked a question… is it Is?'

'No. It isn't Is and it isn't Isn't.'

'Can't you help me?'

'I better warn you: I can only tell lies.'

'Oh... please! You only tell lies. And you're going to say

that you have a brother who only tells the truth. Well get on with the damned riddle then; I know the answer.'

'I'm not going to say I have a brother who only tells the truth.'

'Well what the devil are you going to say then?'

'I have a brother who only tells the truth.'

'Oh, it's hopeless.'

'It's not hopeless. I *can* help you.'

'That means that you can't because it's a lie.'

'It isn't, it's the truth.'

'Oh, shut up.'

'Your name is Cornelius.'

I paused. He had told the truth.

'But you said you can only tell lies.'

'That was a lie.'

I heard a stifled metallic snort of a laugh, which I knew well. It was my steel soul which has a wry sense of humour, and as I could see, was in cahoots with the sentinel.

'Well if you can help me, then help me.'

He looked very directly into my eyes. His own were filled with compassion, something I hadn't expected. They were like Fredericks's eyes. And I saw that he was Fredericks in ethereal form. He had helped me once, when all else were mocking. He pointed steadily across the plain. 'You can't go to Was, but you can see it. And you can't go back to Is, until you have. Look!'

I looked where he was pointing and saw something menacing in the distance. I didn't like it.

'What is it?' I asked.

'It's the Skeletope.'

'What is a Skeletope?'

But Fredericks's eyes became urgent. 'Go, go, now!' I knew I had to. But I turned as I went, and threw back. 'You were right. He *was* defeating his own argument. The First Cause must have a cause so it can't be the First Cause.' He smiled, and I marched off toward the artefact he had pointed out. He shouted after me. 'His argument was wrong, but it doesn't mean his conclusion was wrong.' He didn't need to tell me that – I knew it.

The clouds seemed to be clearing, and the Skeletope became clearer, and grew in size as I got closer to it; the nearer I got the less I liked it. It was some kind of skeleton, a human one, but far greater than human-sized. I slowed; I had not been at home with skeletons, since my sister had told me that the skeletons that we had seen in the Horniman Museum came alive at night, and one would come to visit me in my bedroom when I was asleep. They were skeletons illustrating the progression from ape to human and they frightened me. 'It will put its *breaky* hand on you, and wake you up,' she had said.

I dawdled to a standstill. But then I heard the rasping voice of command from behind me. 'Pull yourself together.' I knew Allenby might appear at any moment and dispatch me to Wasn't, if I faltered again, but I couldn't move. The great bones were shining in the returning sun, and the menace of the thing froze me to *my* bones. Suddenly Allenby was standing ten feet to my right. He was pointing a pistol at me.

'I am about to issue you with an order, airman. Failure to comply with an order given in the presence of the enemy will result in your being shot through the head, immediately.'

I tried to move, but my legs seemed to weigh as much as a fully loaded shipping container. I heard him cock the weapon. But then came another voice.

'It's alright, Field Marshall. I can take care of this.'

I turned and saw Wing-Commander Banks saluting Allenby. Allenby returned the salute and re-holstered his weapon.

'Thank you. Spares me an unpleasant, but necessary duty.' Allenby turned on his heel and strode off.

'Now, Cornelius. You do have to go up that, but it's quite simple; there are steps cut into the left leg, and they will take you up to the skull. You go inside and look out of the eye sockets. And you will see.'

'I don't know if I can, sir.'

'I know you can. It's no harder than climbing into the nose wheel compartment of a Vulcan. No harder than removing a test gear. That wouldn't have been difficult.'

So, he had known. Maybe the pilot *had* seen it hanging there. And Banks had vetoed the charge, which would have put me in Colchester.

'If you don't go up, you'll regret it for the rest of your existence.'

I came to attention and saluted. 'Yes sir, thank you, sir.'

Then my legs took over and I was climbing the bony steps up the fibula... there was nothing to it.

On up the tibia, across the pelvis, onto a hand, up the lower arm. I noticed signs that both the ulna and the radius had been broken in the same place at some point in the past. It took a few moments for this to sink in. Then the shock hit me. Impossible. But I could prove it or disprove it very easily. I stopped climbing and walked across the rib cage, clinging to the rib above the one I was walking on. I got to the other arm and looked down. Yes! I could see the back of the hand. Sure enough, there was the healed break in the knuckle. The knuckle I had broken twenty years before, when I dreamed I was looking at a gargoyle, in the middle of a church door. Yes, I know you don't get them in the middle of church doors, but in a dream you can. A brass one in that case. As I looked, it started to move toward me, like a snake coming out of a hole to strike me. I punched it hard and woke up to find I had hit the wall above the bed with my fist. My doctor told me I had broken a knuckle. 'And I'm just waiting for the 'wall' to come in,' he had said wittily, meaning that I - a sixty-year old telecom researcher - had really punched another person, and made up the 'wall' story.

So that was it. I had broken both bones in my left arm at age fourteen, and a knuckle in my right hand at age sixty. The Skeletope was *my* skeleton! I was crawling up myself! Friends had often suggested that I was indeed 'up myself', but I always thought that was just a cruel allegory. This was real; I resumed my climb, noting it was just discernible that the very tangible bones were, in fact, enveloped in a ghostly body. I could make out no details, no flesh, no organs, just the slightly flickering pale hologram-like shape of the body in which the bones were clothed. From a distance it had been invisible.

I climbed on, hardly noticing the shadowy ghost of the body. Up the arm, across the clavicle, and into the mouth cavity. Inside I could make out the teeth, but directly above me the bone was as ethereal as the body was outside. I clambered into the space and made my way to where I could see out of the empty sockets. I walked to the left eye socket and looked out.

I saw a very young child in bed, chunks of broken plaster lying around him, a mist of white powder in the air. He could see the stars where the ceiling had been. The person who became the sad ghost rushed into the room and gathered up the child. Then I saw the child and his two sisters wearing Mickey Mouse gas-masks crouching in a narrow wooden shelter, with a woman trembling as she pumped air into the baby-sized gas-mask which enclosed his baby brother. A strange little black creature, with a lot of legs, ran out across the floor of the shelter. The woman stamped on it with a sound of revulsion. The boy developed instant arachnophobia, a syndrome I have, in addition to my nostalgitis. I heard the wailing of the all-clear siren as dawn came. I saw the man whose eyes had been full of fear, now radiating hostility, as he slapped the small boy, who had sallow skin and dark hair. I saw the three children again, two girls and a boy, the boy collecting shrapnel, the older girl calling to children on the other side of the road, 'Sticks and stones may break my bones but words will never hurt me.' They hurt me though; were we bad? Or were they? I saw the empty place where little Valerie had sat; we had been the two youngest of the class, but she had gone forever one night, her only testament an exercise book open at a page with three flower spikes on it, and written in painstakingly neat script was her caption, *A pea family.*

I heard a mumbling aircraft, whose engine seemed to stop suddenly - the woman was white and stiff with fear, the boy had never seen that before. Then I heard a bang and her face relaxed. Then I saw the woman who had been in the shelter, now in tears, in a busy street, in an academic town, with her four children, now homeless evacuees. A priest had his hand on her shoulder and was saying, 'I may be able to get you somewhere.'

I saw two pleasure steamers slowly cruising along the river that flowed through the academic town. On one, was the boy with the woman and his brother and sisters. On the other, were men in blue uniforms, many with bandages, some with missing limbs.

'Who are they?' asked the boy.

The woman answered, 'They are Americans; they are on our side.'

In later life, the boy could never fully join with colleagues and friends when they began to decry these allies, almost no

35

matter what their nation later did. Like the spider whose entire species became anathema after the woman had despatched it, one simple sentence had assured the transatlantic titan forever of the boy's good will.

I saw the child looking out over the great city from its highest point south of its river. A thousand twinkling fiery lights... a bonfire in every street, every garden. I saw a boy outside a clinic, on the first day of a new world, waiting for his brother, who was being inoculated against diphtheria. His face seemed in an ecstasy of happiness, as he looked at a bed of scarlet Salvias, glowing in a flowerbed planted in the middle of the drab bricks and grey paving. He knew it was Peace, and he loved everything about it. I too love it, and everything it pervades, even a tiny park in a small red-brick Victorian town.

I saw the boy smiling in a red cap, sitting in a bus with his sisters, which was filled with similar children. Then I saw him again in a blue cap, with a fish badge, waiting to be strapped on the hand, priests walking to and fro in the corridor, where he stood in a queue. Then a man was wandering on a street that sloped up from a wintry shore. The man now had not fear, but worry in his eyes, and wore a battered fawn mac. He was pulling a long log along the ground and each child carried a piece of driftwood. 'Poor wretch!' said a man in a passing car.

Now the boy had a maroon and yellow cap on his desk. He was standing at the blackboard in front of a class debating with a pleasant looking teacher, who said, 'Well, think how useless wings would be when they were just little developing stumps.

Evolution can't have produced wings!'

The boy looked sceptical and mumbled under his breath, 'Have you ever seen a flying squirrel?'

Now he wore a blue cap with white stripes and was standing in a playground. Two other boys approached. The trio looked about thirteen. 'You can punch him, and he doesn't hit back,' said one of the newcomers. His companion punched the boy hard, on his upper arm. The boy didn't give any sign of response but looked sheepish and embarrassed.

The boy was now a youth, standing at a Green Line stop. His two companions were discussing a heavy lorry struggling up the hill, on which the stop stood. The youth contributed nothing. 'They are double acting two-strokes,' said one of the companions. The other nodded.

A different conversation was taking place later, with a group of students who walked toward a pub called the Oddfellows Arms. A heavy lorry passed, and the youth said rather quickly, 'That's a double-acting two stroke'. The remark didn't attract a lot of interest, but some of the other students glanced at the vehicle and nodded. The youth appeared reasonably pleased with the reaction to his comment.

The youth stood under the clock at Charing Cross, as a girl approached him. She had a passing resemblance to an actress called Arlene Dahl, whom she later suggested was more beautiful than other well-known Hollywood stars. They stood on the same station a couple of hours later, having seen a film and sat in Bungee's, a coffee-bar. They were standing close to a train headed for Dartford. 'Well I'll say cheerio now,' the girl said. She looked expectant, but as we all know she who expecteth much receiveth nothing, as was the case. And it turned out that he who diddeth nothing, gotteth it and deservethed it.

The youth was sitting in a moving train. A ruddy faced drill instructor marched down the aisle, barking sporadically at seated recruits. The peak of his hat had been adjusted to slope down, almost over his eyes. 'He's slashed the peak,' whispered a recruit who had had experience of being in the cadet force. The youth was terrified.

'What's your name?' Corporal Shaw bellowed, thrusting his face no more than three inches from another recruit's face.

'Stranks,' replied the recruit.

The drill instructor's face was cold fury as he bellowed, 'Stranks WHAT?'

The youth knew the answer to that question as did all the other recruits except Stranks. The answer was, 'Stranks, *Corporal*.' When the answer came in a mouse-like voice, '*Donald* Stranks,' there was a general murmur of suppressed laughter. After the inevitable explosion, and Stranks' corrected reply, Corporal Shaw turned and sensibly moved on, knowing that an atmosphere of terror is a fragile thing to maintain; but for some reason his glance fell upon the youth who saw in his stern features, a barely discernible sign of empathy with his charges. It took the youth sixty-two years and six months to finally give tangible form to that expression.

The young man looked puzzled. Mr Dubbey had covered the board with symbols. But he was mesmerised by one sentence.

A function f from R to R is continuous at a point p in R if given $\varepsilon > 0$ there exists $\delta > 0$ such that if $|p - x| < \delta$ then $|f(p) - f(x)| < \varepsilon$.

He couldn't understand it. His dreams of being a mathematician were at an end. But he copied it into his notes, and took it back to Blackheath, in despair. That night he stared and stared at the notes, until at last his face cleared, and he went to bed at ten to one. In the morning he smiled to himself. Why had the others got it so quickly, and he taken half the night? Later in life he came to know why. Most of them had guessed that you didn't have to understand it – you just had to be able to write it. The others didn't care one way or the other. He realised that he had a priceless gift: the flaming sword of unquenchable curiosity. But he did wonder: why should anyone give a monkey's toss about continuity anyway? He was only two months on from Vulcans, swearing and crew room banter. But he did find out why, as the days passed. He learned that it was the difference between the real world and the digital world.

Things in the park went on forming and dispersing until finally, I saw the scene I had desperately wanted to see. The woman with the buggy moved across the field of view, this time holding hands with two little figures. A holy trinity. I felt the most lacerating pain a man can know. The pain of love overwhelmed me, as if I had been forced to drink molten gold, straight from a furnace. The love that sleeps, but never dies, usually only rearing its head when tragedy threatens.

I moved hastily to the right eye socket. I saw not Was, but Possibly; I took everything in, and passed out.

I came to, sitting on a park bench. Of Possibly I recalled little, but a strange scene, involving Allenby or someone like him, and someone like Corporal Shaw was in it too. Also, the little boys, who were now adults. They wore grim identical clothes, and it looked as though they were living in interesting times. I hastily gathered myself up and slunk quickly out of the park, which was now filled with children playing, odd mums and other adults looking suspiciously at me.

But I was once again in Is, which wasn't Isn't, which was good, and I aim to make the best of it from now on.

Now, where's the rum?

Cheers!

by *Charles Nightingale*

Blue Storm

I watch the sky fall at night

I lie back down from my window,
it was only a glimpse

I want to write you in *my* colour,
clear,
like light of day,

but mostly
I long for you to show me your face
through all of this rain.

by *Luke Nightingale*

Haunted

Lizzie went back, but it was true: Fern House had gone. The General had it demolished after the death of his mother. No-one knew why, but it was rumoured that he didn't want it left standing to attention, haunted by those he had lost.

Did I dream it all?

She still had the watercolour Tom's mother, a gifted artist, had left her. Two children: herself and Tom, racing over the grass. They were nine-years old. She was taller than Tom then, in the way girls often are, until a boy sprouts like a bolting plant. There she was in the painting, young tearaway Lizzie, charging ahead, plaits flying.

She spent so much of her time in Fern House and its gardens as a child, that Tom's mother insisted she call her Aunt May. Faintly she heard a disembodied voice echoing down the years: *'Can't you two keep still, just for a minute?'*

No, they couldn't; they were dashing headlong towards an uncertain future. Lizzie repeated Aunt May's words, and a woman strolling past with her poodle stopped, stared at her for a moment, then strode off.

On the bench where Lizzie sat, rain began to splatter over the startling headline of a discarded newspaper.

11th December 1936

KING EDWARD VIII ABDICATES

It was only a shower Lizzie decided, putting up her umbrella. She wanted to stay in the park longer.

Her fractured mind wandered back to the first time she had met The General, on one of his periods of leave. He'd caught her scrumping strawberries from the kitchen garden of Fern House, and watched his lolloping dog, Gyp, chase her up a walnut tree and hold her at bay. She could never decide who had terrified her most that day: Gyp or his master?

In the Suffolk seaside town, The General was known behind his back as the Bull, on account of his bulk and his stentorian voice, but Lizzie always called him The General.

Here he was now, as scary as any fairy tale monster, with his son, Tom, standing beside him. Hands on hips, The General roared his great bellowing laugh, and shouted up to her. 'Well, you're a funny sort of creature to live in a tree!'

'It's Elizabeth Price, Pa,' the boy said. 'I've seen her at Sunday School with her sister. They tease her frightfully and call her Scarecrow.'

Lizzie didn't blame the other girls for calling her that; she

43

was beanpole skinny, with long hair the colour of straw, and raggedy mis-matched clothes.

'Come down,' The General said, holding out his arms to catch her if she fell.

Lizzie obeyed, awkwardly grazing her hands and knees on the rough bark. Her freckled face was stained with strawberry juice, so there was no point denying what she had been up to. She stood awaiting her fate, her back against the tree.

'There now, don't be frightened of an old ogre like me,' The General said. 'I won't eat you. Tom, run in to Dolly in the kitchen, and beg a bowl of strawberries. Tell her I sent you, but don't tell her who they're for. And come straight back.'

Tom shot off, with Gyp chasing after him.

Strawberries: all these years later, I can suddenly taste them, smell them, and hear Tom laughing when I crammed the strawberries into my mouth.

'Run off home now,' The General said at last, and Lizzie dashed towards the iron gates.

'Come tomorrow, and we'll play,' Tom shouted after her.

There were other memories of those days. Dark memories of home that she wanted to bottle and cork, trapping them tight, never to be released.

****

Whenever she could, Lizzie stole away from her mother's butcher's shop to play with Tom in the gardens of Fern House, or sit in the kitchen with Dolly the cook, waiting for her playmate to come down from his studies.

Tom was never strong enough to go away to school. The first time I played with him. Yes. The memory is still there, like a favourite snapshot in an album.

'What **was** The General thinking, letting a gangly girl like you come here to play?' Dolly said. 'There's plenty of lads in the town would do as well.' She went on grumbling, while Lizzie waited, hopping from foot to foot, and sighing with impatience until Tom came down, on the drag, swinging a cricket bat that was nearly as big as him.

'You shouldn't keep a young lady waiting. And watch what you're doing with that bloody bat.' Dolly said.

Something like that.

'What young lady?' said Tom, pretending to look around the kitchen. He grabbed a jam tart from the table and Dolly feigned a swipe at his tousled head.

'Outside, the pair of you!'

Dolly. Long dead now. And her sons too. Both killed over there in France.

Lizzie followed Tom onto the grass next to the tennis court.

'Now, look here,' he said. 'I'm Captain and it's my rules.'

Yes, that's what he told me. And I let him believe it.

Lizzie merely spat past him far across the grass, a trick she'd practised with older boys, and Tom had to jump back. She waited, sullenly kicking at daisies while he set up stumps, measuring and rearranging them. At last he shouted, 'Catch!' and threw her the ball. Caught off guard, she fumbled and

45

dropped it.

'Butterfingers! I knew it!' he said, and he snatched up the bat from the grass. 'You bowl. And I suppose I'll have to let you field as well.'

Deliberately, Lizzie aimed a low, slow ball at the bat and Tom struck out. The ball went high and wide. She zig-zagged after it, squinting up into the blue until she was ahead of where it might land. Staggering back and reaching high with one hand, she caught it. Tom whistled in appreciation. 'Not bad!' he said, 'For a girl.'

Funny how I only ever remember one summer day of rain at Fern House.

****

The day began with glorious skies of blue and white, but when the sunshine dissolved into a drumming patter of rain, Tom and Lizzie were forced inside the house.

'Take off your shoes,' Tom whispered, at the foot of the front staircase, 'and don't make a sound. I want to show you something. Mama has gone over to Kirton and won't be back for ages.'

'What if they come back early? We're supposed to stay in the kitchen with Dolly.'

'Dolly's asleep. Come on. Don't be a scaredy cat.'

Oh! the delicious childhood thrill of things forbidden.

They climbed until they reached a back room at the very top of the house. Tom turned a key and pushed open the door.

46

Lizzie followed him in. A great spider skittered over the bare floorboards and a small round window on the opposite wall flew open. Lizzie moved closer to Tom. A brass bedstead and a trunk showed that someone had once slept there. Paper, covered with a faded print of roses, hung in tatters from the walls and black mould made patches on the ceiling.

'Help me,' Tom said.

Together they lifted the lid of the trunk and Lizzie pulled out a white cotton dress with a stripe round the hem, the kind a colonial servant might wear. It was covered with brown stains and she pulled a face and dropped it.

Tom picked it up. 'You can try it on if you like,' he said pushing it at her. 'I put it on sometimes. Dolly said it belonged to Nurse.'

'You're disgusting! Why do you put it on?'

'I don't know, but somehow I always feel better when I do. Sometimes I just hold it against my face.'

Lizzie pricked her ears. She could hear the swish and thud of someone running along the narrow path below, brushing the tall grass on either side. 'Listen! Did you hear that?'

'It's her. It's Nurse. I knew you'd hear her too, Lizzie. Sometimes I see her when I'm unwell, or when I dream. Sometimes she looks in my bedroom window and watches me playing with my soldiers.'

Lizzie shivered.

'Aren't you afraid?'

'Yes, often.'

I heard gossip about you once, after church. They said you had the gift of second sight.

'Do you know Lizzie, sometimes ghosts come from the future and visit us in the present to warn us,' Tom whispered.

'Stop it Tom! You're scaring me.' She pushed him out of her way. 'I'm cold, I'm going back down.'

Home. The dreary little butcher's shop in Hamilton Road, where oozing stains were covered with sawdust.

****

Three small gifts lay on the breakfast table next to Lizzie's plate. It was her twelfth birthday.

'Don't touch them until you've finished your eggs, Elizabeth. Show some patience for once,' her mother, Annie Price snapped.

Lizzie's sister, Alice, took her side whenever she could. 'It's her special day! Let Lizzie open them now mother, please,' she said, glaring.

Annie Price clicked her tongue. 'Open them now then,' she said after a while.

'Happy Birthday, dear Lizzie! Mine first!' Alice exclaimed.

Lizzie tore the paper and found a little notebook, perfect for drawing the small creatures The General showed her.

Eyeing the present she knew was from Tom, she dutifully opened the gift from her mother next.

'A new prayer book. Thank you, Mother.' She laid it aside.

From Tom, two fishing flies, delicately crafted, nestling in a matchbox. Lizzie kept opening it and closing it again until her eggs were stone cold. Annie watched her closely with beady black eyes. 'Of course, you won't be going to Fern House anymore,' she said.

'Mother! Please don't do this! It's her birthday!'

Widow Price swooped on Alice now. 'You'd be happy for her to hare about like a wild thing forever, with that haunted boy. Anything for a quiet life that's you, Alice, and another thing...'

Lizzie sat stunned while her mother pecked away.

'Well, I'm not having it, d'you hear? We never get anything out of it. It's time she helped in the shop more.'

Lizzie scraped back her chair and leapt up. 'But The General promised to take us sailing over at Bawdsey today, for my special birthday treat! And Alice can come too if she wants to. You want to come don't you Alice? Say you do. If you don't let me go Ma, I'll hate you for the rest of my life!'

'Hate me then,' her mother said coldly. 'You'll thank me one day.'

Alice tried in vain to comfort her sister.

'Don't cry Lizzie. Please don't. Remember, you *never* cry.'

*Remember. Remember never to cry. Push it all
down. Screw it as tight as you can.*

Later, when The General's trap arrived for Lizzie and Alice, the neighbours looked impressed; their mother let them go.

****

One afternoon, in her shop, Annie Price looked up from a

49

marble slab where she was hacking at a bloody piece of meat. The General stood before her, tapping his great thigh with a riding crop.

'Mrs. Price, would it be possible for Lizzie to come and play with Tom again? He's still often unwell and she does him good.'

Annie bit her lip. She looked down again and continued chopping. What would be in it for her? She could turn this request to her advantage. Lizzie was of little use in the shop.

'She's needed in the shop all the time now. The likes of us folk must work. I'd have to get a lad in, and who would pay for that? Times are hard.'

From his changed expression she could see that The General understood her, and she was right; without hesitation, he offered to pay for a boy to help out. The General said she needn't worry; his wife would act as chaperone.

****

Lizzie remembered how, after the trip to Bawdsey, Tom had seizures more often, some debilitating enough to confine him to bed. Although The General sought the best medical advice, there seemed to be no explanation for them. She could never understand why he didn't use the village doctor.

One spring day Lizzie crept up the stairs of Fern House alone, to Tom's room. She sat on the edge of his bed eating his grapes and spitting the pips at him.

'You won't be able to come on the church outing now. When are you going to be better?'

Tom shrugged. Lizzie looked around his room.

'I suppose we could play with your soldiers on the bed if you sit up a bit more. Where's the tin?'

'Over there on the shelf, by the window. Be careful! Don't knock that jar off, it's got my stick insect in. Pa found it for me. He said we could sit behind your mother in church one day and put it on that black hat she wears. You know, the one with feathers.'

'The old crow,' Lizzie said, and they both giggled.

Tom pushed back the bedcovers and raised himself up with what little strength he had. His forehead was beaded with sweat and he coughed. Lizzie got up and reached for the tin, but froze when Gyp jumped off the bed, growling at the window. Something white was falling slowly, silently to the path below.

'Did you see that Tom? Did you? You must have seen it!' Lizzie pressed her nose to the window-pane.

'It's no use looking,' Tom croaked. 'I doubt if she'll come again while you're here.' Sinking back in his pillow, he pulled the eiderdown up to his eyes, muffling his voice. 'I'm tired. You better go home.'

****

In her teenage years Lizzie visited Tom's home on a regular basis, sharing his studies and learning so much from The General and Aunt May, that she began to look forward to teaching in the local school. She tamed her wild appearance, and gradually childhood games with Tom in the garden

51

became lengthy discussions of hopes and dreams in the summerhouse.

Posters went up all over town. 'Your country needs YOU!' they proclaimed.

'But they don't need *you* Tom. Please don't go.'

Lizzie pulled her shawl about her. A wind had sprung up from nowhere, whirling dead leaves about them. 'Won't you stay Tom? Not even for me?'

He nudged her affectionately. 'Not even for you Lizzie. Pa's pulled strings and I've passed the medical, and I wouldn't have it any other way. Got to do my bit you know.'

'But I've got a bad feeling about it.'

Tom laughed. 'You and your feelings. What a silly goose you are!'

The summerhouse. A dove flapped in and fell to the floor, dragging one wing. We couldn't save it.

****

Christmas came, and Tom didn't come home. He wrote, but he could never get leave.

In the kitchen Dolly passed Lizzie a tin bowl of potatoes. 'Peel these. And properly mind, don't go leaving any eyes in. It's unlucky.'

Lizzie kept her head down as she spiralled the skins and dug out the eyes with the point of a sharp knife. Finally, she plucked up the courage to ask, words rushing out. 'Dolly why do roses scent the house and garden, even in the dead of winter?'

'Ask me no questions and I'll tell you no lies. Pay no mind to Tom. He's not well.'

'Is that why he once had a nurse?'

Dolly gave Lizzie's hand a sharp tap with her wooden spoon. 'Look, young lady, there are some things that are no business of yours!'

Lizzie wasn't put off. 'We see her, you know.'

****

The years. Where have they gone? The King has abdicated. Another war is sure to come.

Lizzie got up from the bench in the park, collapsed her umbrella and shook herself. She had a little bedsit on the seafront where she was going to meet Alice. She needed to go back and make herself presentable or Alice might worry. As she walked the sky cleared to a beautiful watercolour blue like the blue in Aunt May's painting, but a voice squawked that it was all her fault that things had gone so wrong all those years ago. That she was a curse.

Back in her garret she turned the knob and lit the old gas fire. How kind of Aunt May to leave her the watercolour in her will. It brightened the dingy room.

Children racing over grass. But where is Gyp?
Oh! There he is, out of frame. The General too,
pruning his roses.

She felt faint and breathed in short gasps. A voice was calling.

Howzat! Catch Lizzie catch!

53

In the cramped room she reached up, snatching at air.

Butterfingers!

It grew chill, in spite of the fire. Something sighed and a spider dropped from the ceiling and skittered over her feet. Lizzie reached for the edge of the table, but fell back, knocking the watercolour from the mantelpiece to the floor. The glass shattered.

> *Summertime at Fern House. The knock of a ball on a bat, the drifting sound of laughter, the scent of roses. It's summer now forever. They're all here in the park: The General and Aunt May, Dolly and Gyp... And me and Tom. And she's here too, Nurse, haunting the whispering grass and the trees, watching us play.*

****

June 1917. A telegram brought news of Tom's death at Coxyne.

A few weeks later Aunt May sought out Lizzie in the summerhouse and silently put a letter beside her on the bench, before walking away. Trembling, Lizzie set down two spiders she was letting run over her brushes and wiped her fingers before opening it.

Belgium May 1917

My dear Lizzie,

Just a few pencilled lines. There isn't much time, although we will be glad to be moving out and doing something after all this hanging around in an infernal limbo. I cannot pretend with you Lizzie, I feel like a bad angel, fallen from heaven into hell. Nothing grows here but Death. I would give anything to be back in the summer house reading Ovid with you.

The old seizures are back, and Nurse haunts this unholy ground. I have seen her ghost several times, but don't worry dear girl, she is here to look after me, just as she always did. I must make Pa proud and then come home.

Now I know how precious life is and how little time we all have, I want to share my secret with you. When I come back from this god forsaken place, I mean to tell your sister Alice how much I love her. She has no idea, but I have loved her ever since we all went sailing that day at Bawdsey. I mean to be her husband if she will have me, and a true brother to you.

A splendid plan, don't you think?

Goodbye for now dear girl.
Affectionately as ever,

Your Tommy

by **Robin Greene**

Ghost

What strange lady is this

So free from curiosity,

All the world at play behind her

And she does not turn to see.

by *Luke Nightingale*

The Jelly Bottom Twins
and the Allen Bees

For David

A story for children
and adults who long to play in the park.

Contents

Illustrated by Diane Rich

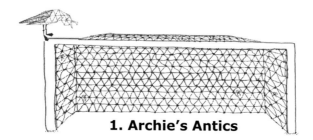

1. Archie's Antics

Archie reckoned the herring gull perched on his goal post could smell the cold chips in his pocket. Herring gulls were his favourite seagull. He loved them for being big, sleek, and fearless. The two things he liked best though were their daft pink knobbly knees, and the way he could see straight through their nostrils when he looked at them sideways.

Archie called the seagull Dontfeed because of the signs along the seafront. He'd saved the chips from last night's supper to give Dontfeed during the match.

Pulling his sleeves down to cover his wrists, he shook them till his fingers tingled inside his goalie gloves. He spat on the palms, left first, then right, and jumped up to grab the crossbar. Hanging from it, he tried to hook his legs over, so he could crawl along to feed the seagull a chip.

'Kwaa-aarrrk!' kwaarrrked Dontfeed.

Archie looked up. *Bother,* he thought. *Coach is heading this way. Annoying Nikesh is coming too.*

The annoying boy was never far away from his dad on match days, following in his speedy wheelchair, as usual. Everything about the chair was striped black and yellow, even the metal frame and wheel spokes. If that wasn't enough to show he supported the Allen Bees, Nikesh could make his chair buzz when he wanted to sound an alarm.

'Get down Archibald Bottomly!' said Coach. 'What do you think you're doing? Try and LOOK like a goalie at least.'

Nikesh piped up in his high pitched voice. 'Yes. Like my dad says, try and look like a goalie.'

'Sorry Coach,' said Archie, wishing the annoying boy would bumble off. Still clinging on with one hand, he swung his legs and pretended to practice goal kicks. *Just because Coach lets Nikesh wheel up and down the side-lines, he acts even more snooty than he does in class. That boy behaves like he's a bossy match official*, thought Archie.

Coach pulled up the zip of his tracksuit top with an angry zzzzpppp. He folded his arms and glared at the team's goalie.

Ketchup dripped from Archie's free hand. 'Oooops. Sorry Coach. Caught red-handed,' he said, wiping sticky sauce over the three black stripes on his yellow jersey. Coach pulled his, I-am-not-amused face, so Archie stuffed the chips back in his pocket. Dontfeed would have to wait.

Dontfeed shook his feathers and protested. His *splat!* just missed Coach's head so Archie tried his best to look angelic. 'Sorry Coach.' he said.

Coach stayed zipped-up and glaring. 'Is that all you can say? I don't think you're taking this game seriously, Archibald. You're letting the Allen Bees down.'

Archie held his breath to stop himself from sorry-Coaching again. 'I'll try to bee-have better, bee attentive, and bee a good goalie, Coach,' he said. 'Bee-lieve me, I will.'

He jumped down and did his best to stand in a goal-saving pose: knees bent, back slightly hunched, eyes fixed ahead, hands in front with fingers spread wide.

'Hey, Dad! I'll snap that rare sight,' said Nikesh, laughing. He didn't get a chance because Dontfeed swooped down fast and pecked the phone from his hands. 'Hey!' Nikesh yelled, as it landed in his lap. He watched the bird circle overhead, and the *splat!* as it slithered down the yellow and black flag clipped to his arm rest. 'Hey! Get the ref to give that bird a red card can't you, Dad?'

Archie bounced lightly on the spot trying hard not to laugh. 'I am taking the game seriously Coach, of course I am. It's the last game of the season, after all. I want the Bees to be top of the league and win the trophy.' He air-saved a ball to convince Coach he was up for anything the Walstowe Wanderers might send his way. 'And I want Mattie to score the two goals she needs to break the Allen Bees' goal-scoring record. Me and Mattie want the name *Matilda Bottomly* in their hall of fame. And I really do want my sister to be crowned Queen Bee.'

'And I really want all that too,' said annoying Nikesh.

Coach frowned. 'The way you and that nuisance bird are carrying on, the only place the *Bottomly* name will go, is into the Hall of Shame.'

'The shame of it,' said Nikesh, annoying Archie even more.

'Archibald, if the referee catches you messing around, he'll send you off,' Coach warned. 'We've lost two players already. Two Stowes in the first ten minutes, stretchered off with their mysterious injuries. Things are serious. I don't want any of my Bees going off, and certainly not for stupid antics. Don't forget: This. Game. Matters!'

Archie replied in a small voice. 'Sorry, Coach.'

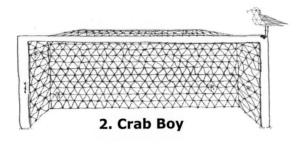

2. Crab Boy

Archie hoped that bouncing more vigorously would make Coach satisfied enough to buzz off to the other end of the pitch. That would get rid of Nikesh too. The other end was where the action always was, thanks to Mattie's brilliance. But Coach didn't budge, and his son stayed put, watching the game, transfixed.

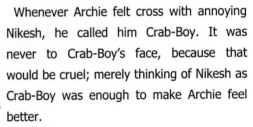

Whenever Archie felt cross with annoying Nikesh, he called him Crab-Boy. It was never to Crab-Boy's face, because that would be cruel; merely thinking of Nikesh as Crab-Boy was enough to make Archie feel better.

Apart from painting team colours on Crab-Boy's electric wheelchair, Coach had tampered with the wheels. It meant his son could move sideways up and down the pitch, always facing the action. And it meant the supporters opposite never got to see the secret extra platform Coach had fixed to the back, or know how often he stood on it to get a lift up the pitch.

Archie put thoughts of Crab-Boy aside and watched Mattie almost dancing with the ball in the Walstowe Wanderers' half. She dodged tackles, kicked up-and-over Stowe heads, and saw off any player who could keep up with her. Nikesh let out a cheer louder than anyone as Mattie managed her signature move.

'She's doing a nutmeg!' he shrieked.

'NUUUUUTS!' yelled Mattie, before kicking the ball through the defender's legs and running around to carry on dribbling. With one more nifty foot flick she booted it into the goal.

When it whammed onto the back of the Stowes' net every Bee supporter yelled, 'BEE STIIIINNNG!' and Nikesh buzzed his alarm.

'Mattie is the bees-knees!' shouted Archie, punching the air. 'She's un-bee-lievable.'

Coach leaned in towards him. 'Try to be more like your sister,' he said. 'And don't you let her down, today of all days.' With one more zzzzipppp he jogged away to join the rest of the Bees.

Nikesh switched his super wheels to sideways mode. He sped along crab-like, and waved at all the supporters on the other side of the pitch. From the spectator zone the gleeful Allen Bee fans waved back, and the gloomy Walstowe Wanderers fans ignored him. The buzz of his whirring yellow and black spokes mingled with the cheers of the Bee supporters. Nikesh joined in, his sweet voice singing out across the pitch, and his thin arms waving to conduct the chant, 'Go Bees! Go Bees! BUZZ, BUZZ, BUZZ!' Swaying together, Bee supporters sang until they were giddy.

Dontfeed trampled his pink webbed feet on the crossbar. He tipped his head back, opened his beak wide, and let out a loud, 'Kwaa-aarrrk!' Archie couldn't help jumping up to dangle from the crossbar again.

Even though he was one of the Allen Bees, Archie had never liked football. It was his mum's fault he was a Bee. She'd insisted that if Coach wanted Mattie to play in the local team, Archie must be the goalie. She promised that Mattie was so good her son would never need to leap into action, and she was right. Archie was pleased that he never got a chance to save a goal and didn't mind that in matches all he did was muck about, with no-one but Dontfeed for company.

Still dangling, he stretched out an arm to offer the seagull a chip. Instead of grabbing it, Dontfeed spread his wings and splatted. Coach was watching. Archie jumped down. 'You're the best defender a goalie could wish for,' he whispered.

Staying low gave him a chance to watch ants climbing up his goal post. Their speed, the way they suddenly halted, and never crawled in straight lines, fascinated him. A long sharp blast from the referee's whistle jolted him back to the game. Another player was down. From the way Coach was hovering around, it looked like a Bee was in serious trouble.

Clangs came from the ambulance parked behind Archie's goal and the doors opened. Two paramedics climbed out. As they strode onto the pitch, Archie feared the worst.

Please, oh please don't let it be Mattie.

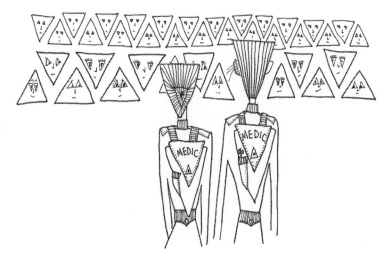

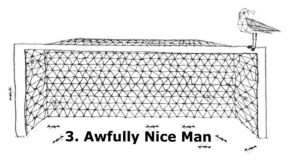

3. Awfully Nice Man

Whispers rippled through the spectators.

'Oooh. It's that lovely paramedic again.'

'Such an awfully nice man.'

'Awfully nice.'

'So VERY nice.'

'Thank goodness for the awfully nice man.'

'He's absolutely charming.'

His charm worked on everyone: the supporters, the players, the referee, and even Coach. They all seemed tranquil and unworried, just as they had been when the two Stowes went down. The awfully nice paramedic convinced them all, including Archie, that behind his medical mask was someone caring who could fix any injury. With a nurse there too, Archie felt even more comfortable about things. Instead of doing his usual worrying about Mattie, he looked for grass cuttings to cover up Dontfeed's splats.

Crouching down, as if in a trance, Archie took off his goalie gloves and swept his fingers over the pitch. The feel and smell of grass always helped make playing for the Bees bearable, but something wasn't right; this pitch felt like his gran's old green carpet and looked like it too.

Ah! I remember, he thought, *since our last home game, the council has revamped the pitch. They've gone and laid some*

66

rotten not-grass-at-all-stuff. Archie had so many objections to it. What was wrong with him? Why did he feel the need to list them all when Mattie might be injured?

... 10. There are no daisies to pick.

... 32. There are no mud-puddles to slide in after it's rained.

... 83. Where will insects live?

... 105. Should I call grasshoppers 'hoppers' now?

... Infinity. My lists never end.

Ants scurried over the not-grass, in all directions trying to find a way in. Loyal Dontfeed protested on their behalf by delivering another *splat!*

Saving insects is far better than saving goals. Archie opened his gloves to catch them.

'I'll carry you to a new grassy home. Come on you little fantastics,' he said.

Enticing some into the finger holes, he kept at it until Mattie's voice snapped him out of his trance.

His stomach churned as he remembered the injured Bee.

'Did you see it, Archie? Did you see Jagdip go down?' said Mattie, out of breath from sprinting the full length of the pitch.

'No. I missed it. I was...' He clamped his gloves shut to stop the truth coming out.

'Weren't you even worried it might be me?'

'I tried to be but...' Archie couldn't understand why he had been so distracted. Of course he was worried about Mattie. He always looked out for her. 'I'm glad you're safe, Twin Sis.'

'Jagdip. Our best player,' she said, caring and modest as

usual. 'He'd just passed me the ball - great cross, and I could have scored, but he stopped in his tracks and went all floppy. It was horrible, Archie. It's exactly what happened to Mike-the-Strike and Inger-the-Winger. Don't you think that's odd?'

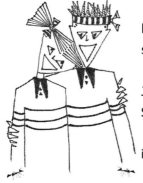

Archie swallowed a gasp. 'Jagdip. Our best friend,' he said, letting the news sink in.

Mattie stroked her brother's arm. 'Yes. Jagdip's the third player this game. Two Stowes and now a Bee.'

'That makes it 2-1,' said Archie, instantly wishing he hadn't.

'This is serious,' said Mattie, sounding like Nikesh. She rolled her eyes at him, the way she always did when Archie said something stupid.

'But that nice paramedic will help. And the nurse too. We don't have to worry, Mattie.'

The awfully nice man raised his arm for attention. Instantly the crowd hushed. 'No need to be worried,' he called out. 'It's just a case of seasonal exhaustion. It's merely football flop. This is not uncommon at the end of a season.'

'Ahhh,' sighed the spectators, adoring the paramedic with their glazed eyes.

Archie's tensed muscles relaxed. Sighs and whispers of, 'awfully nice man,' and, 'nice man, so charming,' drifted in the air again, as Jagdip was lifted onto the stretcher.

Archie smiled, but hadn't meant to. He let out a wail and shook his right hand. 'Ow! Stop that!' he said, meaning it.

Mattie looked at him, puzzled. 'What? I didn't DO anything.'

'Not you, Twin Sis. THESE. One bit me.'

He pulled back his glove and she peeked in. 'Oh Archie! This is no time to start one of your insect collections.'

'My goal is to save these ants. That paramedic's not the only one on a rescue mission,' he said, waving his glove in the direction of Jagdip, who lay very still.

The paramedic's soothing voice was loud and clear. 'Trust me. There is nothing to worry about,' he said. Archie exhaled and his worries vanished.

Nurse tucked a blanket over the patient, then she and the awfully nice man carried the injured boy off the pitch.

Mattie seemed immune to the charmer. 'Where's Jagdip's mum?' she asked, scanning the supporters. Archie looked for her too, not bothering to check for his own parents; they always worked at their hair salon on match days.

'There,' said Archie, spotting Dontfeed hovering above the Bee spectators. Mattie followed her brother's gaze to Mrs Patel, who was chatting cheerily.

'That's strange,' said Mattie. 'You know what a fusser Jagdip's mum is. How come she doesn't seem bothered? It's like everyone's been hypnotised or something.'

She waited for her brother to reply, but he was busy guiding ants into his gloves. 'Hmmm?' he said, peering at the way their legs moved. He snapped out of it when another ant nipped him.

Dontfeed marked Coach out on the half-way line with a near-miss splatter.

'Look at Coach,' said Mattie. 'He's laughing with the referee about that seagull. That's not like him.'

'You're right, Mattie. Why isn't he more interested in Jagdip?'

'And why doesn't the ref care about three brilliant players stretchered off before it's even half time? There's something strange about this game, Twin Bruv. Something's not right about that paramedic.'

Archie stroked his ant-filled gloves. He looked towards the ambulance in time to see the doors slam shut, with their good friend Jagdip stowed away inside.

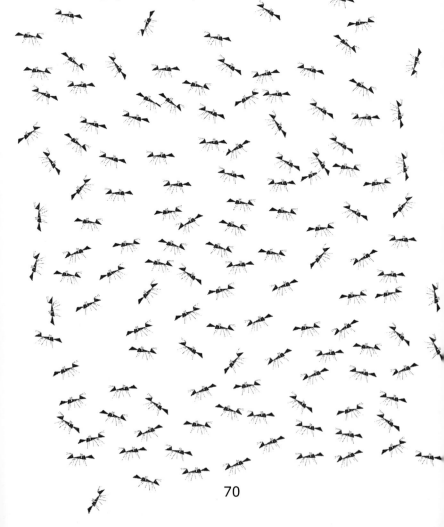

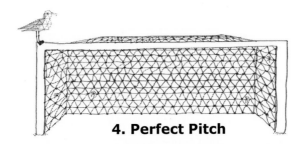

4. Perfect Pitch

By the time both teams were ready to play on, the ants inside Archie's gloves were so agitated, he could barely keep his arms still. He mimed juggling three footballs, an exercise he'd invented in training sessions, but it sent ants down his sleeves and under his football shirt. Things got worse when ants from the pitch crawled over his football boots, up his socks, and along the yellow stripe of his sporty black jogger bottoms.

*So many ants want to be rescued! Whatever I do, I mustn't **ant**agonise them.* He sniggered at his own joke.

Coach was back to his old self. He sprinted over, and Archie braced himself.

'What's the matter with you, Archibald? Your fidgeting is getting worse. You've got to keep still, or you'll distract our best players. Do you want to put your sister, Matilda, off her game?'

Nikesh rolled up, sideways as usual. 'It can't go on,' he said, in his annoying way.

The more Coach and Nikesh complained, the more Archie wanted to make up ant words, and laugh. *Coach is having a **r**ant,* he thought. He dug his teeth into his top lip so he wouldn't start tittering, but the tickling ants were too much. Hopping from foot to foot was the only thing for it.

'Pull yourself together, Archibald. You look like you've got ants in your pants.'

'I have actually Coach,' said Archie, adjusting them carefully.

Coach breathed out long and slow, as if his goalie had exasperated him. He shook his head, then jogged off to cheer on the rest of the Bees.

Anxious not to get a red card, Archie closed his eyes and tried to put the fidgeting ants out of his mind. Voices behind the goal made him turn. What luck! Near the ambulance the paramedic was talking to Nurse. Earwigging on hushed whispers would be a good distraction. Archie got into his goalie pose and leaned back to hear news of Jagdip.

'Three of the very best down. Well done, my dear. Things are going to plan,' said the paramedic in his soothing voice.

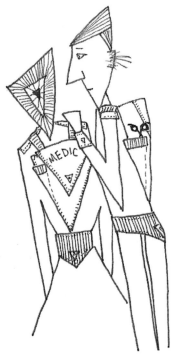

Nurse replied in silly giggles. The charmer went on with more smooth talking. 'My dear, the way you programme our super-secret-sting-rynge, I'm very impressed. They never miss their target. And don't you just adore the players' startled faces when they've been stung? Still and obedient, the way you like children to be.'

Frightening though the words were, they didn't bother Archie. All he wanted was to hear the charming-calming voice, no matter how shocking.

'Then the foolish footballing

hopefuls wilt. And that's where we come in to pick them up. It's genius. Could you programme one more stinger, my dear? Oh, please say you will. Pretty please?' he said.

There were more giggles, flattered and frivolous ones. The sort Archie found more irritating than the wriggling ants.

'You have the most perfect timing, and perfect aim, my dear. And every sting most perfect, just like you, my perfect dear.'

With everything so perfect, Archie didn't bother to worry, but when the shock of another ant bite brought him to his senses, things changed.

Ouch! Mattie was right. Things ARE serious. That paramedic just said 'super-secret-sting-rynge' and 'perfect aim'.

'Soon my dream team will be complete. All I need is one more top player - that last brilliant Bee, and we'll have the perfect team, my dear.'

Alarm bells clanged in Archie's head. *One more top player? That last brilliant Bee could only mean one person.*

'Off we'll go to my secret training camp to give intensive mindlessness training,' said the charmer. 'Next year the season will be mine, all mine. I mean ours, all ours. There won't be a cup, trophy, or medal I don't own. I mean, we don't own. Right now, I couldn't do it without you, my dear; not without you and your programming skills. You are the perfect stinger.'

WHAT? Archie wasn't going to let them stop Mattie becoming Queen Bee.

And he wasn't going to let anyone sting-rynge her.

And NO-ONE was going to take his sister anywhere.

When Nurse spoke, Archie knew the voice. He tried to think fast. *Whose voice is it?*

'Of course I'll do it for you, dearest. I'll programme any sting-rynge to hit anyone. Oooooh, how could I resist your charms?' said Nurse in a soppy-sweet tone. It got worse when she spoke in rhyme. *Who else does that? THINK Archie!*

'Let me make it crystal clear:
Because of you,
My perfect dear,
A sting-rynge and I,
Will always be near.'

'Poetry. Perfect poetry,' said the smooth-talker. 'We will win

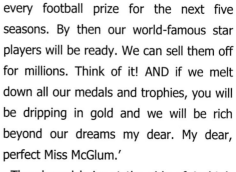

every football prize for the next five seasons. By then our world-famous star players will be ready. We can sell them off for millions. Think of it! AND if we melt down all our medals and trophies, you will be dripping in gold and we will be rich beyond our dreams my dear. My dear, perfect Miss McGlum.'

The shaved hairs at the side of Archie's head bristled, and the curls on top straightened.

Miss McGlum?
How could it be her?
MISS McGLUM!

Without a doubt it was Miss McGlum's voice.

This was terrible news.

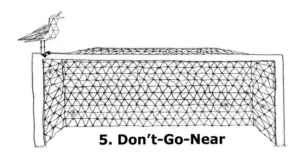

5. Don't-Go-Near

Archie wasn't surprised that Miss McGlum was in on a very wicked plan. What did surprise him was that teachers had another job at weekends.

His teacher, Miss McGlum, a stretcher bearer? He'd never seen her lift even a finger in the classroom.

His teacher, Miss McGlum, dressed as a nurse? He'd never known her do anything caring.

His teacher, Miss McGlum, at a football match? She hated sport. Her idea of a P.E. lesson was twenty minutes playing Dead Lions; anyone who moved got punished with a sit-still detention.

His teacher, Miss McGlum, had a friend? Surely not a boyfriend? Why would ANYONE like Miss McGlum?

The ants seemed disturbed by it all too, which made Archie's wriggling worse. That was when Miss McGlum went back to using the strict, shrill voice of the classroom; nothing sweet or giggly about it at all.

'I recognise that wearisome wriggling,' she shrieked from behind Archie's goal. 'Archibald Bottomly. Did you hear any of that very p-rrrrr-ivate conversation?'

Archie turned to face her. 'No Miss McGlum. I can't even hear you now,' he said. *Ooops. Bother. Stupid mistake by me*.

'Stupid mistake by you, Bottomly,' said the paramedic in his silky tones.

Archie gulped as the charmer stepped forward. He had never sniffed a paramedic, but this one didn't smell the way he thought one should. There was no hint of clean about him, or anything disinfectanty, just the smell of stale tobacco and rotten old socks. It was the same smoke and mouldy cheese stink that the man down the road had; the man who went off to London every day to do his super sales job. It wasn't a nice smell, but it was hard for Archie not to want more of it and follow him to catch another whiff. That was one reason he and Mattie gave the man a name; they called him Don't-Go-Near.

Feeling light-headed from the stinky wafts, Archie steadied himself. His seagull hovered overhead. Apart from Dontfeed, there were so many *don'ts* in Archies life that he didn't like. His list was endless. Of all the *don'ts*, the one that frightened Mattie and him the most was Don't-Go-Near.

As well as his smell, Don't-Go-Near had other unattractions that could keep you transfixed. He had a hairy ear; one lobe was almost furry, with three long hairs sticking out like whiskers on a cat. Once they caught your eye it was hard to resist hanging around to try and stroke them. If that wasn't enough, there was also Don't-Go-Near's brown stain on his front tooth. A tooth-map Mattie called it. Was it a map of the United Kingdom? Or New Zealand, the wrong way up? The only way to puzzle it out was to keep staring. Archie shuddered; the nice-horrible smell, the tooth-map, and the lure of the furry ear always filled the twins with fear.

Thoughts of Don't-Go-Near vanished when Miss McGlum pulled out what looked to Archie like a regular syringe, the sort doctors use to inject patients or give babies medicine. Focussing better, he saw a mini touch pad on the side.

'We'll have to sting-rynge this boy immediately,' she said. 'We need to stop him leaking our plans.' She gave a shrill laugh.

'Oh, it will be such a joy

To sting-rynge the rear

Of this wriggling boy.'

To Archie's surprise, the charmer took Miss McGlum's hand and teased the sting-rynge away. 'Now, now, my dear. We don't want to waste the very last dart on that wriggling worm, do we?' He folded his fingers over it and tucked it into his pocket.

'But I MUST put an end to all that wriggling,' shrieked Miss McGlum.

'Come now. I'm sure you agree dearest, our super-team is no place for a boy without talent.'

What the awfully nice man said wasn't flattering, but his words still didn't upset Archie. All that mattered was listening to more of the very relaxing voice and sniffing the air.

The ants in Archie's gloves were the opposite of relaxed. They grew so twitchy they were hard to control. 'Ouch,' said Archie, rubbing his wrist. 'I told you to stop that.'

The tiny, sharp bite was the shock Archie needed to realise that, once again, he was being taken in by the awfully nice man and his charm. The lingering tingle helped him see things clearly.

There was a lot to see.

Things like... a hairy ear lobe.

Things like... three long whiskers sticking out of it.

Things like... a tooth-map on his front tooth.

Things like... the awfully nice man was awful, and he wasn't nice at all.

77

Without a doubt, it was Don't-Go-Near.

Without a doubt, Miss McGlum had fallen for his charms.

And without a doubt, Archie wasn't going to feel sorry for her.

The knowing expression on Archie's face set Miss McGlum quivering with rage. She turned to Don't-Go-Near. 'I insist, we simply CAN'T have that nuisance of a boy buzzing off and spilling the beans on us,' she said. Opening her nurse's bag, she fumbled inside, then spoke more slowly. 'Isn't it lucky that I carry a spare sting-rynge?' She pulled it out and laughed, witch-like.

Don't-Go-Near's eyes narrowed, but Archie's widened.

'How clever you are, my dear,' said Don't-Go-Near.

Miss McGlum set to work programming the sting-rynge. Her nails clicked frantically on the touchpad while Archie shook his hands to get relief from the agitated ants.

'STOP THAT WRIGGLING! How can I do my important programming with a wriggling boy putting me off?'

The way she was talking, fast and frantic, made him wonder if she had a fever. She tried to out-stare him, like she did in class, but her eyes kept shifting to his waving hands. She wheezed as her words poured out. 'A wriggling boy like you- a- a - wriggling boy like you... one like you- your type, you could...

78

easily wriggle right out of your skin. Yes. And then where would you be, eh?' She turned to Don't-Go-Near and shrieked, 'WHERE WOULD A BOY LIKE HIM BE, IF HE WRIGGLED RIGHT OUT OF HIS SKIN?'

'I don't know, my dear. I couldn't say,' he said. His voice was ice cold, while McGlum's was hot and hysterical.

'EXACTLY. We wouldn't know WHERE he could end up. He'd be a jelly bottom on the loose. I couldn't have that. Not in my class.' She tapped at the sting-rynge, her fingers in a frenzied blur. 'This will fix him. This will keep him still.'

Archie watched, bemused. Knowing that the paramedic was Don't-Go-Near was bad enough, but seeing him and Miss McGlum plotting together, like two crazed-scientists, made his skin shiver and his mind whizz. *Miss McGlum never said we could wriggle out of our skin in last term's 'The Skin You're In' project!*

'I'll stop you boy. I'll stop you becoming a jelly bottom and wriggling out of this,' she said, with a sinister screech. She muttered calculations, then read out letters as she typed them in.

'B. E. E. L. I. N. E.'

Don't-Go-Near smiled a sickening smile. 'You are quite right, my dear. We must stop him.'

The sight of Don't-Go-Near's puzzling tooth-map made McGlum's frenzy worse. Fingers shaking, she worked away, and spat words at Archie. 'Don't think that you can wriggle right out of your skin and escape, Archibald Bottomly. And DON'T THINK I would let you take your sister with you. Oh no. Don't even DREAM it. WE'RE having her! You can't wriggle away with Mattie. No. No you can't.'

Miss McGlum waved the sting-rynge at Archie like it was a

79

school playtime bell. 'Sting-a-ling-a-ling!' she said. 'No more playtimes for you, Jelly Bottom. Soon your sister will be ours.'

Pointing the sting-rynge at his rear, Miss McGlum pulled back the stopper.

'I'll put a sting in your Bee tail,' she said.

With a triumphant look on her face, she fired.

'Matt-ieee-eeee!' screamed Archie, darting away.

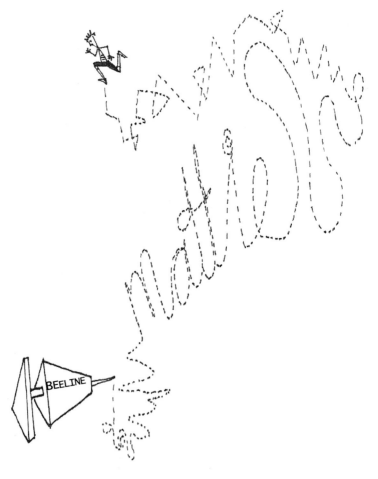

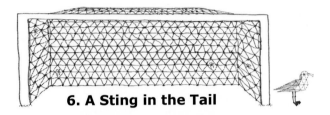

6. A Sting in the Tail

Archie ran out of his goal faster than he'd ever left it. Thanks to Miss McGlum, he knew exactly how to save Mattie, but he needed to get to her. Changing direction, stop-starting, dodging, left, right, left was very important to his plan. He wriggle-ran, the way he'd seen his ants move, mixed with the waggle-dance of bees. If he could keep it up, there was a chance the sting-rynge might not find him before he reached Mattie.

Archie's desperate Matt-ieee-eeee wail, with a special shrill wobble at the end, was the signal the twins had agreed to make in a real emergency. Mattie turned the instant she heard it. She ignored Coach's frantic protests, and the alarming buzz of Nikesh's horn. She shot towards Archie, dribbling the ball as she ran. She was fast-footed, skilful, nifty and in no time domineering the Bees' half. Confused Stowes followed in hot pursuit, with their captain giving orders. 'Mark her. Everyone! Mark that Bee. She's up to something. Get that ball!'

Brenda, the Stowes' defender, left her usual position in front of the goal. Roly, the Stowes' goalie, joined in too. Mattie took no notice of the Bees' pleas to, 'Pass, pass, the ball.' She had no time for that. She wove her way round every human obstacle and sped towards her brother.

The referee increased his pace and ran alongside, fumbling with his whistle.

All eyes were on Mattie as both teams swarmed round her, desperate for the ball. They hurtled towards Archie in a bundle. *I've got to reach my sister before the sting-rynge strikes.* He lunged left and right, as he tried to get a view of her through the tangle of Bees and Stowes.

Miss McGlum started a new chant which the Stowes sang with gusto. 'Jelly, jelly, jelly,

Bottom, bottom, bottom,

Jelly Bottoms melt away,

Until they are forgotten.'

I don't care about mean Miss McGlum, or if the Stowes forget me. But I DO care about saving Mattie. WHERE IS SHE?

'Kwaa-aarrrk,' kwaarrrked Dontfeed, flying right above her.

'Let me through!' yelled Archie, trying to push everyone away.

Dontfeed splat-bombed two players. Even though they fled, Archie was still blocked. His despair mingled with tickles that spread all over his body. Ants crawled down his jogger bottoms, out from the cuffs of his sleeves, the collar of his football shirt, his gloves, pockets, and from anywhere an ant could politely hide. They headed towards the players on the pitch, biting their way through Bees, 'Ow!' and Stowes, 'Ouch. That hurt!' They didn't stop nipping everyone until they had cleared a path for Archie to reach Mattie.

Don't-Go-Near was racing towards Mattie too, medical bag on his back. He kept up his charming act and called to the referee and spectators. 'Nothing to be concerned about. I anticipated this. I have everything that's needed, for those bites. Stay calm please. I have antiseptics, antihistamines, anti-biotics, and if necessary, I can mix up an antidote.'

The crowd fell for it. They sighed as their favourite paramedic rushed to the rescue; they swooned at the sound of his soothing voice; they whispered their usual awfully nice man murmurs too.

Face-to-face with Mattie, Archie had no time to explain because Don't-Go-Near pulled out the very last sting-rynge from his paramedic pocket. 'I can apply this one manually,' he hissed, sneering across at the twins.

'In his hand, Mattie!' shouted Archie. 'DON'T-GO-NEAR!'

Mattie didn't disappoint. She spun in the air, jumped like an antelope, back-flipped her whole body and twist-flicked her best kicking foot, aiming the ball right at the villain. Her kick knocked the sting-rynge from his hand and it soared up with the ball, higher than the trees. Players and spectators looked skyward.

'What goes up must come down, or have you forgotten that lesson, Archibald Bottomly?' said Miss Mc-glowering-Glum. She was ready, holding open her medic's bag to catch the falling weapon.

Archie cried out, 'Nooooo!'

'Kwaa-aarrrk,' kwaarrrked Dontfeed. He swooped to catch the flying sting-rynge in his beak, then flapped teasingly low over Miss McGlum's head.

'A bird. A bird. Get it away from me,' she shrieked, running towards the ambulance.

Dontfeed dropped an on-target *splat!* then flew off, with his beak clenched around Don't-Go-Near's secret stinger.

'My hair,' wailed Miss McGlum, as the seagull's goo spread over it. She clambered inside the ambulance. The clang of the door was masked by loud cheers from the Stowe supporters as they watched the football plummet from the sky. It landed in the

Bees' goal. Jubilant Stowes cheered and praised the Bottomly twins for levelling up the score with an own goal.

On the side-lines, the referee blew his whistle. He ignored the chaos and got stuck into an argument with Nikesh about whether the goal would count towards Mattie's Queen Bee score. Nikesh was insisting it must, of course.

Don't-Go-Near leaned against the goal post. 'My wrist. You've broken it, you wretched girl,' he stammered under his breath. He bandaged his bruised hand and flapped his elbows to shake off ants. 'I'll prepare another sting-rynge for you, Queenie, as soon as I'm fixed. You're coming with me!' He made a grab for Mattie with his good arm.

'Oh no you don't,' said Archie. He lunged forward to reach Mattie, but the angry Bee players ran between them, singing their new chant. 'Mattie! My hand, my hand. Take it, Mattie!' Archie grabbed at the air, hoping he would find her. 'Hold my hand, Mattie. Feel for my glove. Grab it! It's our only chance to get out of here.'

Determined, Archie would do exactly what Miss McGlum feared; he'd wriggle out of his skin and take Mattie with him. Through his goalie gloves, he sensed a hand. Relieved, Archie loud-whispered. 'It's time for me to jump, Mattie. And you're coming with me. Don't let go. DON'T LET GO!'

He waggle-danced for luck then shouted, 'One. Two. Three... NOOOOOOWWWWWW!'

At that exact moment Archie felt the sharp sting of a dart in his rear. *The cheek of it,* he thought.

7. Great Escape

I did it! Wow! It worked, just like Miss McGlum said it would. I've escaped. I must have wriggled out of my skin just before the sting-rynge went in deep enough to give me football flop. Wow!

Archie grinned and whistled softly, relieved that everything seemed to be intact and in its place. He stared at his hands, fascinated to see that the skin was slightly pinker than usual. His lips tingled the way they did when he used his dad's toothpaste. He licked them lightly as he searched for the freckle that always helped him work out which was his left hand; there was no sign of it. He let out a long breath, thankful not to see any of the ghastly capillaries and underneath stuff that Miss McGlum had made Class 5McG learn for their horrid end of term spelling bee.

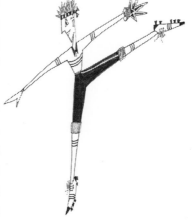

Looking up, Archie marvelled at his hollow self, thin and still on the pitch. His emptiness stood like a wax statue, frozen in an energetic goal-saving pose, both arms

85

stretched out in a perfect diagonal line. One dipped towards the ground with its gloveless hand reaching forward, and the other behind him, pointing skyward.

Thanks to all his bad-spelling detentions, Archie knew that skin had two top layers. Had he really wriggled out of one? How was that possible? What a buzz it gave him to think no-one would know that his smart Bee kit was simply held in place by his top epidermis. And what a relief that nobody noticed all the odd things about him.

1. Instead of being in his goal, Archie was mid-field.

2. He was absolutely still.

3. He had a remarkable posture.

4. With nothing inside him, he was empty and stick thin.

Even Nikesh hadn't spotted them.

Stretching and flexing his new fingers, Archie remembered his right glove. It wasn't on the pitch so he shifted his eyes to look in the bushes. *It must be here somewhere. But where? And where is Mattie?*

Archie was about to search for her when Nikesh shouted out, 'Hey everyone! Look at Archie!'

Oh no. I'm a rumbled Bee, he thought. Spectators and players turned to stare, but no-one looked his way.

'So statuesque,' they murmured in astonished voices.

Jeering Stowes scoffed, laughed, and mimicked Archie's stance. 'He looks more like a dancer than a goalie.'

'Ha, ha, haaa! Yeah. The Bees' goalie is a right prancer.'

They scarpered the instant Dontfeed landed on the knot of the hollow Archie's bandana and

86

flapped his wings. Coach wasn't put off. He walked round the statue, tutting and shifting his zip up and down. 'I've never seen anything like this before,' he said. 'It certainly isn't another case of football flop.'

'It's more like football freeze,' suggested Nikesh, wheeling up close. 'Is there such a thing, Dad? Is there?'

The referee butted in. 'I'll ask the authorities,' he said, making notes.

'Archie's so still,' Nikesh laughed. 'It's almost  thrilling! Miss McGlum will never believe it.' He went to take a snap but stopped when Dontfeed glowered down.

The referee got back to his squabble with the boy, insisting that Mattie's last goal would NOT count in her Queen Bee score. Brenda-the-Defender broke up their argument, asking where that awfully nice paramedic was and the glum nurse.

Archie blinked to focus and catch sight of them. He strained his ears to hear the referee's answer, but the scene went blurry and the familiar voices faded.

Wow! Where's the pitch gone? I don't recognize that tree! Where am I? And where is Mattie?

8. Bee Wear

Scrambling through the mass of bushes without getting scratched was going to be difficult. Archie kept his arms close to his sides and breathed in to make himself thinner. He went to leave the shelter of the leaves and branches but heard a voice. Holding his breath, he tried not to move; someone was peering in his direction. They were rolling up a veil of black netting that went all round the wide rim of their straw hat. Once the netting was fastened, Archie saw the face of a friendly looking boy. He was taller than Archie, maybe ten or eleven, or just big for his age.

'Eyes left,' said the tall boy.

Archie obeyed orders and, once he'd worked out which way to turn, looked left.

'Mind the…' The tall boy paused mid-sentence, the way an army sergeant keeps a squadron in suspense, waiting for an order.

'…birds.'

'Wow!' said Archie. 'A nest in the bush. Oooh. Blackbirds, aren't they? My grandad taught me all the eggs.' He leaned over to look inside it, then through the tangle of leaves at the tall boy. 'Don't worry. I won't touch them,' he said.

The tall boy looked relieved. 'Glad to meet someone else with ornithological identification skills; a fellow bird lover is always most welcome here. Mama will be delighted.' He reached across and started to pull the branches aside to clear the way for Archie to step out. He stopped when Archie shrieked.

'Oh no! Don't look! I've lost everything Bees wear! EVERYTHING Bees wear!'

Letting go of the bushes, the tall boy ducked down. 'Beware? Beware of what?' he said, jerking his head left and right, looking all around as if he expected an ambush.

'No. I mean I've lost my Bee wear; my kit for the Bees.' Archie pushed his knees together and did his best to hide anything he didn't want seen.

'Kit? You mean like a soldier's uniform?' said Edmund.

'Kind of. It's what I wear when I'm with the Bees.'

'Are you a beekeeper?'

'Erm... I'm a keeper for the Bees on Saturdays when I play for them.'

'You play for them? Ha. How simply marvellous. That is music to my ears. What do you play? Which notes soothe the colony?'

Archie opened his mouth to explain, but a bee flew up and he snapped it shut. The tall boy waved it away with his long-armed beekeeper gloves. 'Mama has beehives. It is my job to maintain them and collect the honey. I tend the hives every day whilst on my school vacations. At school I board. And you?'

'Bored at school? Yes. Often.'

The tall boy smiled. 'Birds, bees and boarding. Three things we have in common. How marvellous. Here old chap; take this. Take my bee wear.'

He handed Archie the garment he'd been carrying over his arm. 'I have completed my chores for today, and there are beekeeper smocks a-plenty in the house. Consider it yours.' Archie waited for the stranger to look away, then flapped and scrabbled to put it on. The kerfuffle in the bushes didn't stop the tall boy's chatter.

'I had to smoke 'em today to calm the little blighters.' He squeezed the leather bellows on his copper beehive smoker, and a curl of grey smoke twisted in the air. Archie shuddered when the scent of it reached him.

'It is merely smoke,' said the tall boy, putting the smoker on the grass and lining up his large beekeeper gloves alongside.

The hem of Archie's old-fashioned smock reached his ankles. He was glad of it but wished it wasn't like his Great Aunt Edith's nighties. The same embroidered honeycomb pattern across the chest tickled at first, but a few cotton threads were nothing compared to wriggling ants. Once dressed, he jostled out of the bushes and thanked his new friend.

The tall boy walked towards Archie with a swagger. He picked two leaves and a twig out of Archie's spikey hair, then stepped back, nodding approval as if inspecting soldiers on parade.

'All present and correct,' he said. 'Awfully pleased to meet you. I'm Edmund. Edmund Allenby, from the Allenby Estate.'

Archie took in the view behind Edmund - a shrub-filled garden with fine lawns, over-hanging trees, and a mansion-style house. Two black horses stood on the pathway by the front door, harnessed to an old-fashioned carriage, the sort Archie had seen in the Sunday evening T.V. series his mum liked.

Mattie loves horses. She's bound to pop out soon with this pair on show. She is, isn't she? Isn't she?

'My mother is Catherine Anne Allenby,' said Edmund. 'She lives here. And you are?'

'I'm Archie. Archibald Bottomly.' He cleared his throat and added, 'Of the... Coronation Estate.'

Edmund raised an eyebrow. 'Coronation? I like the sound of that.'

'My mother is Barbara Bottomly. People call her Babs.'

'A Lady?'

Archie nodded. 'Oh. Yes. She's definitely a lady.'

'How pleasing. Mama is so fussy with whom I mix. She is most determined that I meet a Lady one day.' Edmund held out his hand.

'Best not shake hands,' he said. 'Sticky epidermis. Sorry.'

Archie wished he had his gloves. *There was definitely only one on my goalie statue. Mattie must have my other one. She'll have*

91

grabbed it when I pulled her with me.

He looked back at the bushes for signs of her but saw none. *She'll be hiding, cross 'cos I dragged her out of the most important game of the season. WHERE IS SHE?*

Wondering whether not shaking Edmund's hand had caused offence, Archie saluted him instead. He'd never saluted anyone before, but there was something about Edmund that made doing it seem just right. His new friend looked gleeful and saluted back.

'What year were you born, Edmund?' said Archie.

'1861, old boy. That makes me almost eleven. And you?'

Archie tried not to gasp or cough. 'Oh. Er... 1861? You were born before me,' he said, fighting the urge to jump about. *I haven't just wriggled out of my skin, like Miss McGlum said I would; I've **time**-wriggled out of my skin. This is the best history homework ever. Wow! I'm a real-life Doctor Who.* He looked round, hoping to glimpse a TARDIS, but wanting even more to see Mattie.

This must be the park where the Allen Bees play their home matches. Wow! Me and Edmund are standing where my goal is.

He imagined Miss McGlum, guarded by Dontfeed, looking out from her ambulance prison at the perfectly still and silent hollow Archie. He was glad to be free of his mean teacher, and of Don't-Go-Near too, but gladder that he'd saved Mattie.

WHERE.

WAS.

SHE?

9. Blown Off

Edmund pulled at some loose netting on the rim of his floppy straw hat. It didn't look like a hat for beekeeping; it looked like the sort of thing a gardening grandma would wear. All the clothes Edmund wore made Archie feel less bothered about having to wear a baggy dress.

Are they... tweed knickerbockers? Wow! They look itchy. No. They're velvet. Yuk! Long socks tied with ribbon at the knee; there's so many buttons on his jacket, velvet too, it must take him forever to get dressed in the morning; that big sailor collar covering his shoulders will get in the way when he does a handstand. His boots? Oh my! They're too dainty, laced up too high, and so pointy they look too tight to be comfy. Ouch!

Edmund caught him staring at them. 'You are without footwear,' he said, pointing at Archie's bare toes.

'I don't mind.' Archie shuffled his feet in the lush green. 'My feet get hot. This lovely grass is cooling.'

That's bare feet explained, but how can I explain turning up with no clothes at all? Archie stammered, thinking up an excuse as he spoke. 'I w-w-was... wearing my full Bee kit when I set off this morning, b-b-but...'

A light breeze soothed his face and he smiled. 'It's windy

today and my clothes got blown away; me too.' *Phew!* If his fingers hadn't been stickier than usual, Archie would have crossed them; he didn't like telling lies. He shifted from side-to-side, holding out his smock to mimic a kite flailing in the breeze.

'Force 6 due later, Archie old boy,' said Edmund. 'Look at those clouds. Too strong for estuary sailing, otherwise I would be out on the Deben. I do not much mind though. Always happy here, watching the birds and insects. I like to check their nests and hives are extra secure before any high winds.'

Archie nodded. It was the sort of thing he liked doing too.

Edmund gathered up his beekeeper tools. 'I must return these to the potting shed.' He replaced his headgear with an eight-piece cap that matched his velvet suit. 'Do accompany me. And then come to the house. I shall find you some appropriate clothes before Mama catches sight of you dressed that way. She is a most formidable lady; thinks children should be seen properly attired, and not heard.'

Not another glum one, thought Archie, hoping they would

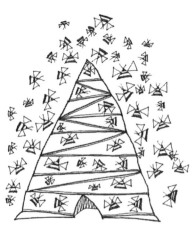

never meet. He didn't want to go into the house; the park he knew didn't have one, so he tried to distract Edmund with questions about bees.

'Have you ever been stung?'

'Very rarely. I have my bee wear and smoker. Mama's bees only sting if their life is threatened, or to protect their hive. It hurts, but when I pull out the sting, things get back to normal rather quickly. Don't you find that?'

Archie decided that 1871 wasn't ready for a lecture on bee sting allergies, EpiPens, or his mum giving him half a paracetamol for pain, so he just nodded. He walked beside Edmund and took in many fascinating bee tips. While he listened, his eyes darted from bush to bush searching for signs of his Allen Bee sister. Everything Miss McGlum had said about wriggling out of his skin had been right so far. Surely that meant Mattie must be near. Archie was convinced of it. All he had to do was find her.

'Has anyone else new blown in, Edmund, apart from me?' he said.

'Only that ant on your left sleeve.'

'Ant?' Archie stretched both his arms out and watched an ant crawl onto his cuff.

Edmund stiffened. 'Hold on. What have we here? STAY BACK!' he said, putting on a protective bee glove.

'It's my pet,' Archie joked. 'We go everywhere together.'

'You do? How very impressive.'

The ant paused, probing some delicate stitches with its antennae. It was nothing like the black ant-dots Archie was used to. 'Wow! You've grown. It looks like you've had a ginger tint too!' he laughed. 'I promised I'd find you some grass, didn't I? Here.' He spread his arms wide, showing off the spectacular lawn. 'Isn't it fantastic?'

'I suspect this is no ordinary ant,' said Edmund. 'Allow me to take a closer look.' He pulled a silver-handled magnifying glass from his velvet pocket and leaned towards Archie's sleeve.

While Edmund studied the ant, Archie got back to looking out for Mattie. Where was she? His search was cut short; in only a few minutes, Edmund's face beamed with the happiness of an explorer finding treasure.

'Scrutinise those fine mandibles, dear boy,' he said, passing Archie the magnifier.

There was something commanding about Edmund, and despite his worries, Archie obeyed orders. Who wouldn't? Scrutinising mandibles was a heavenly idea.

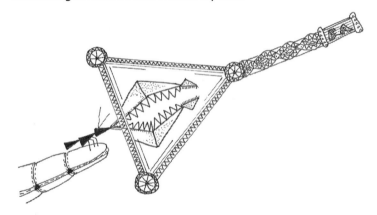

'Those are a pair of spectacular pincers, what?' said Edmund.

Archie nodded, proud of his ant.

'That pet of yours is a soldier ant,' said Edmund, his grey-blue eyes looking lively.

'Really?' said Archie, his nose almost touching the lens.

Edmund crouched down. 'There must be more. Soldier ants are not lone creatures. Help me search.'

The two new friends rifled through the grass together. Being without Mattie, Archie felt sorry for his lonely ant and hoped they'd find more. Edmund seemed to feel the same.

10. Carried Away

As they searched, Archie scanned the garden for Mattie. When there was no sign of her he sunk down in the grass with his head low.

'Are you all right, old boy?'

'I didn't just lose my glove and my Bee kit. I lost the thing that's most important to me.'

'My dear friend, please allow me to help you find it. What am I to look for?'

'I've lost my Mattie.'

'Your Mattie?'

'She's my sister. She's wearing a black and yellow kit, and her hair is tied in bunches.' Archie grabbed the air below his ears to show Edmund what bunches were, in case it wasn't a fashion in 1871. 'I should never have tried to bring her with me.'

Something moved in the shrubbery and they both stood up, startled. 'Perchance this is her,' said Edmund.

Archie's heart fluttered with hope.

'We must split up; you stay here Archie, and I shall take it upon myself to undertake a reconnaissance mission. Be it friend or foe, I intend to find the source of the rustling. Be ever vigilant, old boy.'

Before advancing, Edmund ripped a thin branch from the nearest tree and held it the way a soldier on parade holds a rifle. He paused and saluted, then about turned and forward marched into the bushes, poised like a hunter tracking a lion.

Desperate to find his sister, Archie knew that if Edmund stayed away for long, it was going to be hard to obey orders. He needn't have worried; in no time the bushes shook vigorously, and Edmund reappeared. He held his stick aloft, with the lost glove dangling from the tip. Archie's spirits rose, then sunk when Mattie didn't appear. He told himself to stay cheerful. *It must be a sign that she isn't far away*, he thought as he stretched forward to snatch his glove.

'Don't go near!' shouted Edmund.

'Don't-Go-Near? Where?' said Archie, looking round, alarmed.

Edmund steadied the stick, holding it away from them both. 'Don't go near!' he shouted again.

'Yes. I know. He's a rotter; lives up the road from me. He gets everyone to think he's awfully nice. He was pretending to be a charming paramedic last time I saw him, but me and my sister, we've rumbled him. Is he here?'

'No. I mean, stay back,' said Edmund. He held his arm up to stop Archie. 'That is an order. One nip from these wild soldier ants, and you will most certainly be a goner.'

'Oh,' said Archie, spotting what must have been an entire colony of ants. He took a step back and then sniffed the air. 'Did you set off your smoker in the bushes?'

'I did not,' said Edmund, nodding over to his beekeeper paraphernalia on the grass.

Archie sniffed again. 'And you didn't take your shoes off?'

Edmund didn't answer but stared at the dangling glove. Archie stood on tiptoe to see the spectacle. Ants crawled frantically over the surface.

'They're making a pattern,' said Archie.

'A skeleton hand,' the boys whispered together.

'It's pointing! Look, Edmund.'

'It is indeed. It is pointing into the bushes.'

Archie's heart pounded as they turned to look. *Wow! The ants are leading us to Mattie. They must be!* 'Did you find anyone in the bushes?' he said, almost breathless with anticipation.

Edmund laughed. 'Ha! You must mean the most awful man. Now I think of it, he did have a scent of tobacco smoke and fragrance of unpleasant foot.'

Panic gripped Archie. 'That's Don't-Go-Near. He was trying to steal my sister. You say Don't-Go-Near's here?'

'At ease, dear fellow. I left your rotter being guarded by a few of these feral soldiers.' He wobbled the stick and the ants clung to Archie's glove with their glorious mandibles. 'Fear not, Archie. That villain will be too afraid to move.'

Archie blurted out, 'Didn't you see Mattie? You must have.'

'If the prisoner has knowledge of her whereabouts, I shall get the truth out of him.'

'But how did you know he was the rotter?'

Edmund winked at Archie. 'I have to thank Mama for that. Mama has taught me many sayings to keep me wary of undesirables.' He coughed before reciting them.

'Mama taught me that: *A furry-eared man in the garden shall never be worthy of pardon*.

'And this one: *An awfully nice man who hath charm, doth intend, never goodness, but harm*.

'This one helped greatly too: *No truth lies where a tooth-map lies*.

'Those were clues enough, but when he told me he was your loving uncle, I knew he was a deceiver ever, and that meant I should trust him never, for Mama always says that: *He who lyeth, hath pants that fryeth*. And yes, I could smell smoke.'

Archie was too anxious to laugh or feel relieved that Don't-Go Near was caught. 'Don't-Go-Near is a mean man. What if he stamps on the ant-guards, and runs?' He stamped his foot as he spoke, to stress the point, but when it squelched a little, he wished he hadn't.

'Never fear, old boy. I intend to train all the soldier ants and enlist them for duties.' Edmund stood to attention. 'If he runs, they will round him up with a pincer movement; soldier ants from both sides, up-and-over, then down from top right, and down from top left. The enemy will be surrounded and captured before he can blink.' Edmund lowered the stick and let the soldier ants crawl onto the grass. 'Let me train these beasties up,' he said. 'Once I have the truth out of that rotter, I shall give him his marching orders.' He crept nearer to the pointing glove and shouted, 'Attention!'

Nothing happened.

'Stand in line!' he hollered.

The ants ignored him; they carried on crawling in, up, down, over, and around Archie's glove. Archie had an idea. 'Try this:

Ant-ten-shun! and, St**ant** in line!'

When Edmund repeated the orders, Archie-style, the ants lined up in rows and saluted. 'The ants like you,' Edmund said, throwing the empty glove to his new friend. 'Some might say you must have been good to them in a previous life.'

'Something like that,' said Archie, checking for leftover tiny ones crawling inside.

While Edmund drilled the ants, exhausted Archie dozed in the grass until the sound of marching feet woke him. Edmund was in full command.

'Left, left, left; right, right, right. Left, left, left; right, right, right.' The six-legged crawlers were on the march. Into the bushes they tramped, and out of the bushes stumbled a dazed and dishevelled Don't-Go-Near. He moved towards Archie like a hobbling swamp-man. He squirmed to shake off ants as an army of them gathered round his feet in circles. The first row grabbed onto his trouser legs. The second row fastened their mandibles

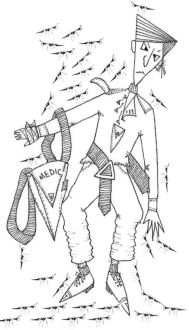

around the ant in front. A third, fourth, fifth and sixth row joined in too.

Fixed together, they pulled, pulled, pulled until Don't-Go-Near fell back, like a patient on a stretcher. The ants crawled beneath him, raised their splendid mandibles, and held him up.

'Mind my hand,' he said, but the ants ignored him. He sat up and smiled a beaming tooth-map smile. His sickly voice was sincere and charming. 'Archibald? Is that really you? Come closer, do. I've been worried about you, sweet boy. Let me take you home.'

Archie gritted his teeth. *Don't look at his tooth. Don't look at his ear. Don't look. Don't look.* He put his hand across his nose, so he didn't get a whiff of Don't-Go-Near's smell when the rotter spoke again.

'Whatever have you been telling your new little friend, Edmund here? And all his nice pests, I mean pets. I think you've been getting carried away, don't you, Archibald?'

Archie replied in a low, slow growl. 'Where. Is. Mattie?'

Don't-Go-Near turned pale. 'I... I thought she was with you.' From the look on his face, Archie knew, without doubt, it was the truth. He closed his eyes, remembering the moment he'd felt a hand in his. *So, it wasn't Mattie's hand at all.*

'Sir, the whereabouts of Mattie is none of your beeswax.' snapped Edmund.

'He's right,' said Archie. 'And anyway, my sister is further away than you can ever imagine. And "*my new little friend Edmund, here*" is going to keep it that way.'

Edmund raised his tree branch baton, then stuck it in the ground. It was the signal for the soldier ants to advance.

Archie picked up the beehive smoker. He squeezed it to get rid of the awfully nice-nasty stench left behind by the prisoner, who got completely carried away.

102

11. Chewing Things Over

The two boys lay in a shady patch of lawn. They looked up at the fast-moving clouds. Apart from when he slept, Archie had never been so still. Chuckling together, they swapped their mother's sayings. Archie dipped the tip of a long grass stalk in fresh honey, leaned back on his elbows and sucked it clean. He chased a runaway drip with his tongue.

'Wow! This honey is delicious,' he said.

'Wow?' chortled Edmund. 'A short but satisfying word.'

'Wow! What you did, training those ants, Edmund. That wasn't just wow! It was wowee-wow!' said Archie.

'And is that what you call impressive?'

'What I mean is, it

looks like you'll make a fine soldier one day, when you're a real *old boy*. Now THAT Edmund, will be impressive.'

'That is certainly not what I want to be,' said Edmund, his expression darkening and his voice sad.

Archie sat up straight. 'What do you want then?' he said.

Edmund stared at the great house. 'I want bees, forever buzzing on the Allenby Estate.'

Archie grinned, feeling proud to be an Allen Bee for the very first time.

'There are other things I should like very much,' said Edmund, his eyes still fixed on the house. 'I desire nothing more than lush grass, right here, for everyone to enjoy. And birds nesting and singing in these trees every spring, and... I fear you will think I am foolish.'

'I won't, Edmund.'

'I want a bed of roses. This garden needs roses. They are my favourite flower.' He waved his grass like a wand. 'Do you think my wishes will come true, dear boy?'

Archie looked towards the mansion, the fine lawns, the bushes laden with bird's nests, and bees fussing over blossoms. 'I do think they will come true,' he said. 'And I promise to help make them happen.' He flipped his right foot onto his left knee. When he waggled it there was another faint squelchy sound. He coughed to cover it up.

'You all right, dear fellow?' said Edmund, looking his way.

Archie ignored the question and asked Edmund what he knew about soldier ants.

'They never stay too long in one place, and they make nests with their own bodies, gripping on to each other with their mandibles.'

'Wow. Fascinating,' said Archie. He shuffled in the grass. 'Will the ants with Don't-Go-Near ever stop marching? I mean, if they stop, where will it be?'

'The army will march until the soldiers get hungry. It could stop anywhere, but it will not be near to Mama's estate, if that concerns you.'

'No. But... What happens when it stops?'

'Then the soldiers will eat something.'

'Oh,' said Archie. 'Are soldier ants herbivores?'

Edmund screwed up his eyes. 'Not necessarily. It depends what's on the menu,' he said.

Archie gulped and stopped talking. He watched the gathering clouds as he thought this through. When he next spoke, it was in a soft voice. 'I don't know how to get back home.'

'Dear me,' said Edmund, sitting up. 'Really? Why not stay here? You still must meet Mama, have luncheon with us, and we can go to the beach; I shall teach you to sail when it's calm.'

'That's quite a list. Thank you, Edmund, but I have too much to do at home. I need to see Mattie, help the Bees find a queen, get rid of Miss McGlum, set the 2-1ers free, give some ants a home, and feed Dontfeed. But before any of that, I have to get back to my old self.'

'That, Archie, certainly is a most impressive list.'

'It's not just that.'

'There is more?'

'Yes,' said Archie.

He stayed quiet for some time, chewing his grass stalk, then took a deep breath. 'I think I'm melting,' he announced.

Edmund peered at him. 'Good gracious. Are you certain of it, old boy?' he said. His eyes grew wide at the squelch sound when Archie waggled his foot. 'Dear me. Is it sore? It may well be trench-foot.' He shifted away.

'It isn't catching; really it isn't,' said Archie.

'I was merely moving to alert Mama,' Edmund insisted. 'She can arrange for Jarvis to fetch the family physician.'

Archie sighed. 'The only cure is going home.'

'Mama will order Jarvis to take you there in the carriage. The Coronation Estate, did you say? It sounds very royal. Jarvis never fails to reach any destination. Mama is convinced his head is full of maps, with every twist and turn noted. He is sure to get you home, old boy.'

A flurry of joy crept through Archie's body. 'Every twist and turn? Twist and turn. That's it!' he shouted. He stood up abruptly and threw his grass stalk over his shoulder. 'If Jarvis is going to take me home... he'll have to catch me first.'

Archie set off across the lawn, dodging, darting left-right-left, stop-starting, right again, twisting and running around in a circle, then zig-zagging away. He could hear Edmund's laughter, not far behind. He closed his eyes and wriggle-ran until he was almost out of breath.

I've GOT to bee-lieve this will work, he thought. Adding one more wriggle to his waggle-dance, he leaned forward and jumped.

12. Still Archie

Archie hid in some Allenby bushes for the second time that day. He peeked out.

'Did you see that?' said Coach.

'What? You mean the way Mattie just missed the ball again? Poor Mattie,' said Nikesh, shaking his head.

'No. I thought I saw Archie on the pitch in a long dress. He was right there, in the same spot where he went all still. Trust me, I saw him, Nikesh. Then he dashed into the shrubs.'

'It couldn't have been him, Dad. Look, there he is, leaning on the goal. You should know, you carried him back there.'

'Oh, it was no trouble. He's lighter than a feather.'

'Just you wait, Dad. Archie will get moving again when the game's over. Till then, there he is, looking like a stupid brainless ballerina statue. What's that called, the position he's in?'

'Arabesque,' said Coach, fiddling with his track suit zip and tutting. 'I'm sure I saw a glimpse of him.'

'In a dress? Please don't tell the referee, Dad. He'll call the game off.'

Coach put his hand on Nikesh's shoulder. 'What would be the point? Five more minutes, and we're done for. The Allen Bees will never win this game unless Mattie gets her spark back.'

Nikesh had the expression of a sad puppy. 'Look at her, Dad. She lost her spirit the very moment Archie went all ballet.'

'Maybe I was too harsh on him. I shouldn't have insisted he stay still.'

'He was behaving like an idiot, as usual Dad. And now he's made it worse. The Bees won't win, and Mattie won't be crowned Queen Bee, and it's all because of her stupid brother.' He wiped his nose on his cuff. 'She's your star player. Please don't give up on Mattie, like Archie has.'

'You're right, Son,' said Coach. He hollered down the pitch, 'Come onnnnn, Mattie! Show them who's Queen Bee.' Turning to Nikesh, he said, 'Join me when you're composed, Nik.'

Through the branches Archie watched Coach jog to the other end of the pitch to cheer Mattie on. Crab-Boy was right; Mattie was playing no better than she did as a toddler, missing the ball when it came her way and tripping over her own feet. The crowd wasn't helping, singing McGlum's Jelly Bottom chant every time she bungled the ball.

Annoyingly, Crab-Boy was right again; it was all his stupid fault. He hadn't given up on her though. He had to fix things for Mattie before the game ended; but first, he had to do some extraordinary wriggling to get back in before he melted away. The trouble was, with Mattie not her best, the Stowes were stealing their way towards the Bees' goal; if Archie made a dash for it, he'd be spotted. If they took a shot and hit his hollow statue, it might crumble. He needed help.

'Pssst. Hey, Nikesh. Pssst,' he said.

Nikesh raised his head, startled. He sniffled and wiped away his tears. 'Who's there?'

'It's Archie. I need a lift. DON'T turn your chair round.'

'What? You're not Archie. Archie is over there.'

'I AM Archie.'

'No. You must be a trickster, or a ghost. My dad said this park is full of both.'

'Well, erm... part of me is over there, but I'm still Archie. I'm definitely not a ghost.'

'But I can see a still Archie in the goal,' said Nikesh.

'Listen, Nikesh. I'm really here, but DON'T look round.'

'Is that because you're wearing a dress? My dad said he saw you in a dress.'

'It's bee wear.'

'Huh? Allen Bees don't play in dresses, not even the girls!'

'It's bee wear. BEE WEAR!'

'Beware? Beware of what?' said Nikesh, ducking down in his chair.

'Oh, not this again,' muttered Archie. He whispered sternly, 'Never mind what I'm wearing. Just don't draw attention to me. Help me, please, Nikesh.'

Crab Boy's hand rested just above his alarm. 'Don't press it, Nikesh,' Archie pleaded. 'Help me make things right for Mattie.'

109

That did it. Without hesitating, Nikesh reversed his chair and Archie stepped onto the fold-down platform at the back.

'Anything for Mattie. Hold on tight and keep your head down,' said Nikesh. As his wheels clicked into sideways mode Archie scrabbled to keep the frill of his smock away from them. They sped off to Archie's goal.

Annoyingly, Archie had to admit that Crab-Boy had been a bit of a superhero. He felt in his pocket for the last twist of Edmund's honey and threw it over his shoulder into Nikesh's lap. 'A thank you from the bees,' he said. 'I'll tell my sister you helped me.'

'Hey, thanks Archie,' said Nikesh. He picked up the twist and sniffed it. 'I'll share this with Mattie.'

'Just don't tell her she's your honey.'

Nikesh laughed. 'I won't. I'll tell her, like honey she's naturally sweet, if that's okay with you.'

Crab-Boy was right again, annoyingly. Naturally sweet was the best way to describe Mattie, so Archie didn't object. He squelched as he got down. 'Thanks Nikesh. I'd never have got here without you. Can't stop to chat. I'm on a rescue mission. As you were.'

Raising his hand in a salute that Nikesh wouldn't see, Archie's fingers touched his forehead. He winced. *Eeuww!* It felt like a soggy wet cushion. He pressed it and droplets of, he didn't know what, sprayed out. There was no time to panic because Macca-the-Attacker was racing into the Bees' half, lining up to take a shot at goal. Archie usually let attackers get on with scoring, but today he couldn't let anything get in the way of his mission to make sure Mattie was Queen Bee.

When Macca belted the ball at Archie's net, Archie hurled himself across the goal and pushed it away.

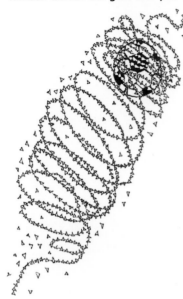

'Caught by the wind,' Macca tutted as it spun off in a whirl of spray. His disappointed eyes stayed fixed on the mist of Archie's gloop orbiting the ball like a solar system of spit; a perfect shield for a boy in a beekeeper's smock to make a dash behind the goal. Now he needed one more distraction so he could creep unnoticed, to his thin statue, and get back in without alarming Dontfeed.

'Coach! Coach! Watch out!' Macca shouted. 'It's heading straight for you!'

'Wha... what? It's raining salty rain!' said Coach, just before the ball whacked him on the head. Dazed, he glanced back. He squinted his eyes to focus on the Bees' goal. 'Get me some water, will you Nikesh? I'm seeing double. There's two Archibalds. Real or not, the one in a dress just saved a goal.'

'The Bees' goalie? Save a goal?' said the referee running up to join them. 'Ridiculous! Coach must be concussed. We need that paramedic.'

Every Bee gathered round with their eyes on Coach, and their ears listening out for the voice of the awfully nice man. Some even tried to sniff him out.

Archie squelched up to his still, hollow self. It wasn't just the

111

sliding-back-in he needed to do. First, he had to find the sting-rynge in his rear; then he had to remove it. If what Edmund said about bee stings worked for sting-rynges too, removing it was bound to unfreeze him in a trice. Wasn't it?

He felt hollow Archie's jogger bottoms with his slippery hands until he found the dart. It was no good; his buttery fingers turned slimier as he pulled at it desperately. He couldn't get a grip and time was running out. What he needed were some pliers, or pincers, instead of his jelly fingers. Archie's melting heart raced as something crawled across his leg. A soldier ant advanced towards the dart and fixed its mandibles around it. More ants marched forwards and lined up behind the dart-gripper. In turn, they wrapped their mandibles around the ant in front, holding onto the abdomen like a tug-of-war team. They pulled, pulled, pulled until the sting-rynge popped out.

Up into the air it flew, caught by Dontfeed, who carried it away.

Now THAT, thought Archie without a doubt, *was a pincer movement Edmund would call most impressive.*

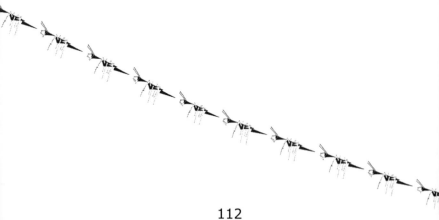

13. Glory Bee

Wow. I'm back! What a relief to be in here again. Especially, when it's such a tight squeeze. Thanks goodness I was a bit sticky, or I'd never have slipped back.

Disorientated, Archie paused to catch his breath. He tried to figure out left from right, and up from down. His squelching had got worse; it was now an unfortunate noise. The sort of noise that made people look down at their feet, and insist it wasn't them. *Did anyone hear me?*

His eyeballs weren't in their sockets yet, so Archie looked out through his left nostril in time to see Mattie's head pop up like a meerkats', the way it always did when she was about to accuse him of something windy. *Was she smiling?* He tried to wave, to signal somehow, but his hands hadn't reached the finger bits.

As soon as the referee pronounced Coach fit to coach, his whistle blew to restart the game. Cheers and stomps erupted from the spectators, so Archie used the noise cover and extra-time to wriggle in. He put all his effort into shoving his elbow into its proper nook. *All present and correct, and ready for duty*, he thought when he was comfy.

He looked out for Mattie again. Glory be! Such relief to see she didn't just have the ball - she was dancing with it.

'She's playing out of her skin,' said Coach.

Nikesh's jaw dropped in horror. Now that Archie's was in the right place, his jaw dropped too.

'Wha... what?' said Nikesh, looking pale.

Coach laughed. 'It's an expression, Nik. It describes someone who's playing exceptionally well.' He tousled Nikesh's hair and they got back to watching Mattie in action.

Nikesh's lone voice, shrill and sweet, sang out like a tuneful chorister.

> 'Go Bees! Go Bees!
> BUZZ, BUZZ, BUZZ!
> Mattie will save us,
> Cos that's what Mattie does!
> Queen Bee for victory,
> Cheer her on and sing with me,
> Go Bees! Go Bees!
> BUZZ, BUZZ, BUZZ!'

No-one wanted to out-sing Nikesh, so the crowd buzz-hummed softly in the background, harmonising and having a good old sing.

With Mattie back on form, and Nikesh as his agent-in-the-field, Archie could abandon the Bees' goal.

'**Ant**-ease,' he commanded. The ants released their mandibles and relaxed. They lined up in formation and saluted Archie when he said, '**Ant**-ten-shun! St**ant** in line'. He ordered them to forward march, and led them towards the ambulance for three more import**ant** pincer movements. Dontfeed flew overhead, hovering to catch the sting-rynge carcasses: first Mike-the-Strike's; second Inger-the-Winger's; third an acrobatic, swooping catch for the Bees' Jagdip.

'Haaaaa-trick!' Archie yelled up to the sky. He gave the faithful seagull a thumbs-up, with his no-longer-sticky thumb. Dontfeed flew a loop-the-loop right over his head and flapped off, with his beak thrice-full.

Overjoyed to be free, Jagdip and the two happy Stowes raced to watch Mattie in action. They stood alongside the singing Nikesh, and buzz-hummed with the rest of the crowd.

Archie issued orders for Miss McGlum to come out from the ambulance with her hands raised. When she appeared, she didn't look old, she looked ancient. The ants surrounded her until Dontfeed returned, empty-beaked. Miss McGlum whimpered like a puzzled puppy, but the seagull showed no sympathy and splat-chased her away.

Climbing up his goal post and dangling from the crossbar gave Archie a better view, so up he went. Coach unzipped his tracksuit top. 'You're still Archie, then?' he called over, cheerily. Archie waved and lined-up some cold chips for Dontfeed.

Glancing away from the action on the pitch, the park seemed small. The Allenby Estate had shrunk, taken up by houses on every side. Archie wondered what Edmund would make of it, and of the new Bees, the children balancing bravely on bright climbing frames, parents sitting on benches rocking their babies in buggies, and dog-walkers telling their precious ones to fetch or sit. The empty space where Felixstowe House once stood made him sad. His thoughts turned to keeping the promise he had made to his friend, until a roar from the crowd got him back to watching the match. Even the trees seemed to be supporting the Bees, their tall trunks cast shadows that spread across the pitch in stripes. *Had Edmund planted them?* Whenever Mattie got near the goal mouth, their leaves rustled, and the crowd cheered wildly, 'Gooo-ooo Mattie! Be Queen Bee!'

Wow. Mattie is unstoppable!

She saw off Rick-the-Kick, and then Laura-the-Scorer (out of position). When she came face to face with Brenda-the-Defender, Archie knew what was coming. 'NUUUUUUUTS!' Mattie roared.

Kicking the ball niftily through Brenda's legs, she dodged round her and whammed it onto the back of the Stowe net.

Roly-the-Goalie was speechless, and Mattie back-flipped in a perfect circle, bunches twirling.'

'BEE STIIIINNGGGG!' everyone yelled.

The referee blew the final whistle of the season with an extra purrrrr-er at the end.

Stowes and their supporters were so overjoyed to see Mattie back on form, and their two best players fit again, they didn't mind losing the league.

The official Queen Bee rushed straight to Archie and hugged him tight. When she let go, she punched his arm. 'Don't EVER do that statue thing again,' she said.

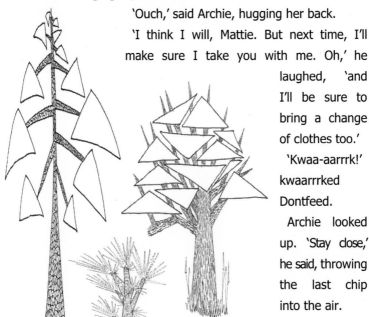

'Ouch,' said Archie, hugging her back.

'I think I will, Mattie. But next time, I'll make sure I take you with me. Oh,' he laughed, 'and I'll be sure to bring a change of clothes too.'

'Kwaa-aarrrk!' kwaarrrked Dontfeed.

Archie looked up. 'Stay close,' he said, throwing the last chip into the air.

14. P.S.

The first thing Archie did when he got home was write a letter.

Dear The council,
Please can we have our real grass back?
It would bexx brilli<u>ANT</u>.
<u>FANT</u>astic.
Some people might like your new stuff, but <u>ANTS</u>think it's p<u>ANTS</u>.
If you need an assist<u>ANT</u>, I will help.
Thank you in <u>ANTi</u>cipation.
From Archibald Bottomly
(A Bee forever)
P.S. Some bird boxes would be nice, too.
P.P.S. And a v<u>ERY</u> lovely rose garden,

THE END

by *Diane Rich*

Synchronicities

Lord Edmund Henry Hynman Allenby

Allenby was born on St George's Day in 1861, in Nottingham, but his life-long love of nature was fostered in Felixstowe, the town of his family home, and where he spent his school holidays. It was at Felixstowe too, where he became skilled in sailing and could indulge his love of messing about in boats.

Educated in Haileybury College, Hertford, then Royal Military College, Sandhurst, Allenby served in the army from 1880-1925. Some knew him as an English soldier, but he was a man with many titles.

Colonel

Brigadier

General

Major General

Field Marshall

Commander-in-Chief in Palestine

British Imperial Governor

1st Viscount Allenby of Megiddo and Felixstowe

High Commissioner for Egypt and the Sudan

Sir Edmund Allenby

Lord Allenby

Whichever way his troops addressed him, behind his back they often called him *The Bull* or *The Bloody Bull*, because of his temperament and persistence. This was balanced out by his reputation for kindness and being known as an intellectually curious man who read books on every conceivable subject from botany to poetry. He had a love for rose gardens too.

As well as his many titles, Allenby was awarded numerous military honours, most notably for his 1918 achievements in Jerusalem.

His only child, Lieutenant Horace Michael Hynman Allenby, MC was killed at Flanders, in 1917, aged 19. Allenby himself died in 1936 and was buried in Westminster Abbey.

Origins of Allenby Park, Felixstowe

Allenby's parents, Hynman Allenby (1832-1878) and Catherine Anne Allenby, nee Cane (1831-1922), bought Felixstowe House in 1862. They lived there for sixty years. The house stood in its own grounds, with spreading lawns, flower gardens and overhanging trees. Allenby ordered its demolition in 1923, after the death of his 91-year-old mother. The site then became Allenby Park. Its entrance lies between residential houses, 39 and 43 Constable Road. There is no house numbered 41.

Lord Allenby, Allenby Park, and links with Joan Rich

Joan has always been interested in history and was delighted to find out about the background of Allenby Park. She has spent more than half her life with views of the park grounds in her sights and even more years with the town of Felixstowe as her home. There are curious coincidences linking her to an Allenby world, starting from her earliest days.

Joan was born in 1918, the same month and year that General Allenby led the climactic battle of the Sinai and Palestine campaign of the First World War, known as the Battle of Megiddo, which liberated Jerusalem. This military achievement resulted in General Allenby being honoured with the title 1st Viscount Allenby of Megiddo and Felixstowe.

Jerusalem not only played a key role in Allenby's life, but in Joan's life too. Like him, she served in the army and was posted to Jerusalem.

Living in Palestine during the 1940s, Joan rented a house with her husband right next to another Allenby Park.

Returning to England in 1948, Joan stayed in Felixstowe for a short time, once again living near to Allenby Park. She then moved to London but came back in 1964 with her four children and lived in a house overlooking the park, where she still lives today. Its closeness to Felixstowe General Hospital was handy as Joan worked there for many years. Because of the hospital's name, and Joan's army background, her twins affectionately called her The General.

When Joan spends time in Allenby Park these days she often remembers the times she was sent there as part of her NHS nursing duties, to retrieve escaped patients. She says even though they were treated very well in the hospital, some preferred to be recovering in the park!

Joan continues to enjoy the flowers, trees, wildlife, and sights in Allenby Park but wishes there were bird boxes in its many great trees.

As this book goes to print, Joan is raising money for the NHS by walking the paths of Allenby Park every day.

Weather permitting, Joan hopes to have completed 102 circuits before her next birthday when she will be 102 years of age. In 2013, aged 95, Joan completed a 5K walk for Cancer Research UK, so this challenge for the NHS should be a walk in the park!

To make a donation visit
 https://www.justgiving.com/fundraising/Diane-Rich1

More locally, profits from the sale of this book will go to the charity Suffolk Wildlife Trust.

About the Allenby Writing Team

Lesley Glaister lived in Felixstowe as a child, in a house backing onto Allenby Park. She is a novelist, dramatist and poet. She has written over a dozen novels, the first of which *Honour Thy Father*, won both a Somerset Maugham Award and Betty Trask Award, and *Little Egypt* received a Jerwood Uncovered Fiction Prize. Usually writing for adults, in 2019 she changed direction when *Aphra's Child,* her first book in a YA trilogy was published. Lesley's stories have been anthologised and broadcast on Radio 4. She is a fellow of the Royal Society of Literature and currently teaches Creative Writing at the University of St. Andrews. Her latest book for adults, *Blasted Things*, out in May 2020, is set in 1920s Suffolk. She now lives in Edinburgh - with frequent forays to Orkney - with her poet husband, Andrew Grieg and an elderly terrier.

Robin Greene was born in 1948 near Rochester Castle, Kent. Before moving to Suffolk in 2008, she spent much of her life in Yorkshire. An early love of literature developed into an interest in writing her own short stories and she joined a Suffolk writers' group. She enjoys creating macabre ghostly tales with a twist. Before the writing habit took hold, Robin worked in early years education as a teacher, and raised her son and daughter. These experiences cemented her commitment to the importance of stories, not only to children, but adults too. Stories aren't her only passion; she enjoys reading poetry and her favourite poet is Emily Dickinson. Robin currently lives in Ipswich. She is a frequent visitor to the Allenby Park area of Felixstowe.

Charles Nightingale was born in 1938, lived through the blitz, the Doodlebugs and the V2s, and grew up in South-East London. Early interest in painting later gave way to science and engineering. After serving four years in the RAF he studied mathematics before joining the BT Research Department, with whom he migrated to Suffolk in 1975. He bought a house in Felixstowe, the back door of which stands opposite Allenby Park. He is married to Dominique Roche and has two sons. He writes, paints in oils and watercolour, makes lino-types and ceramics, and enjoys socialising, cooking, theatre, and concert visits. In 2019 Charles won the Cambridge Invitational Art contest. He regularly exhibits his artwork as a member of the Ipswich Art Society, the Society of East Anglian Watercolourists and the Ipswich-based printing group Inky Fingers. His collection of works can be viewed at *www.charleynightingale.com.*

Luke Nightingale published his first collection of poems, *The Price of Progress*, inspired by his childhood in Felixstowe, when he was 22. Two years later, in 2011, he published a second volume of poetry, *Communal Living*, a collection of epigrams recording his life in London in a hostel housing a diverse population of immigrants, performing arts students, homeless and vulnerable people, and impoverished writers. Readers spoke of his lyrical voice with a deep sense of yearning. Even a poet needs to eat, so after obtaining an MSc in IT, Luke now works at the Francis Crick Institute, a leading biomedical research centre in London, as part of a team exploring the mysteries of mitochondria. The muse continues to accompany him as he explores in his own time the greatest mystery of all: consciousness.

From the age of six **Diane Rich** lived close to Allenby Park, with her mother, twin brother David, and elder brother Douglas. Eventually she left Suffolk to pursue a career in education. As a deputy headteacher, she coached the first football team in her local authority to include girls, and it caused quite a stir! She worked in the education advisory service for Hertfordshire; as a researcher at both Cambridge University and the National Children's Bureau; as a university lecturer; as a trustee for national charities associated with children, and on a variety of radio and T.V. projects. She set up Rich Learning Opportunities and led the *What Matters to Children* team of eminent education consultants. Diane is a member of the Society of Authors, and Faber Academy. She writes books for educators, articles for education journals, and stories for children.

Dominique Roche was born in Bayonne, France, a Basque town famous for its bayonet and chocolate. She studied Classics at Sorbonne University in Paris, then moved to England for adventure. Publications include a fantasy novel, several poems, and regular contributions to *SHE* magazine in the 1980s. In 2014 her poem, *Partir*, was selected to be set to music and performed at the Cockpit Theatre, London for the French Song Cycle Festival, *Voilà*. As well as writing she worked as a Public Service Interpreter for the Police and NHS, and currently runs courses on Greek Tragedy at the Ipswich Institute. She also tutors French Conversation groups. She sings in the choir of Trianon Music Group and plays the mandolin in a folk band. She set up Diatom, a microscopic publishing concern. Of all her adventures, the best has been to seduce an Englishman with the afore mentioned bayonet and chocolate and give birth to two brilliant sons.

Sources:

Lawrence, J. (1993) *Imperial Warrior: the Life and Times of Field-Marshall Viscount Allenby (1861-1936)* London: Weidenfield and Nicholson

https://thepeerage.com
https://www.israel21c.org/ageneralandagentleman
https://www.nam.ac.uk/exploreEdmundAllenby:the bull/National Army Museum
https://www.westminster abbey.org/EdmundAllenby/Westminster Abbey
https://yourbiography.com/edmund-hynman-allenby
Orthodox England. orthodoxengland.org.uk. V 9. Issue 2: 1.12.2005
Wikipedia.en.wikipedia.org/wiki/
Edmund_Allenby,_1st_Viscount_Allenby

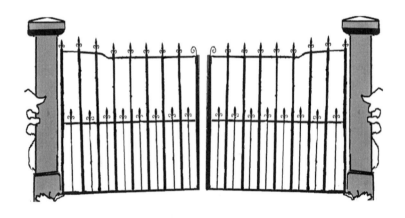